AQA GCSE Design and Technology

C000155596

Graphic Products

Orders: please contact Bookpoint Ltd, 130 Milton Park, Abingdon, Oxon OX14 4SB. Telephone: +44 (0)1235 827720. Fax: +44 (0)1235 400454. Lines are open from 9.00–5.00, Monday to Saturday, with a 24-hour message-answering service. You can also order through our website www. hoddereducation. co. uk

If you have any comments to make about this, or any of our other titles, please send them to educationenquiries@hodder.co.uk

British Library Cataloguing in Publication Data
A catalogue record for this title is available from the British Library

ISBN: 978 1 444 12370 8

First Edition Published 2011
This Edition Published 2011
Impression number   10 9 8 7 6 5 4 3 2 1
Year   2016, 2015, 2014, 2013, 2012, 2011

Hachette UK's policy is to use papers that are natural, renewable and recyclable products and made from wood grown in sustainable forests. The logging and manufacturing processes are expected to conform to the environmental regulations of the country of origin.

Cover photo © Olessya Laskova/iStockphoto.com

Typeset by DC Graphic Design Limited, Swanley Village, Kent

Printed in Italy for Hodder Education, an Hachette UK Company, 338 Euston Road, London NW1 3BH by LEGO

AQA GCSE Design and Technology

Graphic Products

series editor: **Bryan Williams**

David Dunlop

Eamonn Durkan

Geoff Westell

DYNAMIC
LEARNING

HODDER
EDUCATION
AN HACHETTE UK COMPANY

Acknowledgements

David Dunlop would like to thank Pete Marsh, Cannon Slade School, Bolton; Amit Jain, Wellacre Academy, Flixton; Chris Uttley, Culceth High School, Cheshire; Sarah Dunlop, Rivington and Blackrod High School, Bolton; Niall Johnson, Caldew School Dalston; and Steven Parkinson for use of students' controlled assessment work.

Geoff Westell would like to thank Paul Jackson at PPE Ltd and Peter Griffin and his students at Bishop's Stortford College.

The authors and publishers would like to thank the following for the use of photographs in this book.

Figure 1.3 Zaichenko Olga – Fotolia; Figure 1.4 © Digifoto Neptune/Alamy; Figure 1.5 Jim Barber – Fotolia; Figure 1.6 © Cordek; Figure 1.7 Dow – Building Solutions; Figure 1.8 Rob Byron – Fotolia; Figure 1.11 RTimages – Fotolia; Figure 1.12 Car Culture/Getty Images; Figure 1.15 © piai – Fotolia; Figure 1.18 Paperfoam B.V.; Figure 2.6 zea_lenanet – Fotolia; Figure 2.7 Elmer's; Figure 2.8 © Caro/Alamy; Figure 2.10 PPE Ltd; Figure 3.1 Ken Garland; Figure 3.3 OLIVER LANG/AFP/Getty Images; Figure 3.4 © Adrian Sherratt/Alamy; Figure 3.5 S&G Barratts/EMPICS Archive/Press Association Images; Figure 3.6 Photograph by James Veysey, Camera Press London; Figure 3.7 © macana/Alamy; Figure 3.8 © Gregory Wrona/Alamy; Figure 3.10 Photo by Gavin Smith, Camera Press London; Figure 3.11 © Lars Halbauer/dpa/Corbis; Figure 3.12 Robert Sabuda; Figure 3.13 ©David Morgan/Courtesy Robert Sabuda; Figure 4.1 © Peter Widmann/Alamy; Figure 4.2 Rafal Kucharek – Fotolia; Figure 4.3 Marzky Ragsac Jr. – Fotolia; Figure 4.61 © Ian Dagnall/Alamy; Figures 4.67–4.71 PPE Ltd; Figure 4.77 © Shaun-Finch/Alamy; Figures 5.2 and 5.3 PPE Ltd; Figure 6.5 Photo of *Haunted House* by Jan Pienkowski (Walker Books Ltd); Figure 7.1 Fairtrade Foundation; Figure 7.2 © Misko Kordic/iStockphoto.com; Figure 7.5 Roman Milert – Fotolia; Figure 7.7 © Ashley Cooper/Alamy; Figure 7.8 kmit – Fotolia; Figure 7.9 Ruben te Brake – Fotolia; Figure 7.10 Sascha Burkard – Fotolia; Figure 7.12 EU Ecolabel; Figure 7.13 luchshen – Fotolia; Figure 7.15; Nicolas Roche – Fotolia; Figure 7.16; Public Record Office/HIP/topfoto.co.uk; Figure 8.2 © The Print Collector/Alamy; Figure 8.3 © Roland DG; Figure 8.4 © Roland DG; Figure 8.6 Techsoft UK Ltd; Figure 8.8 © Roland DG; Figure 8.10 Denford, denford.co.uk; Figure 8.11 LANDOV/Press Association Images; Figure 8.12 Digital Vision/Getty Images; Figure 8.13a ©Photodisc/Getty Images; Figure 8.13b Rafa Irusta – Fotolia; Figure 8.13c Alexey Goosev – Fotolia; Figure 8.14 © Alex Slobodkin/iStockphoto.com; Figure 8.15 justin maresch – Fotolia; Figure 9.1 © Crown copyright material is reproduced with the permission of the Controller of HMSO and Queen's Printer for Scotland; Figure 9.2 © Crown copyright material is reproduced with the permission of the Controller of HMSO and Queen's Printer for Scotland; Figure 9.3 BSI; Figure 10.3 Rainer Plendl – Fotolia; Figure 10.5 Kallkwik; Figure 10.17 © William Robinson/Alamy; Figure 11.1–11.8 PPE Ltd; Figure 11.10 Stuart Dee/Photographer's Choice/Getty Images; Figure 11.12 Adobe product screenshot reprinted with permission from Adobe Systems Incorporated; Figure 11.13 © johnnyscriv/iStockphoto.com; Figure 11.17 PPE Ltd; Figure 11.20 © Jadehawk – Fotolia; Figure 11.21 © Paweł Sławiński/iStockphoto.com; Figure 11.22 © Techsoft UK Ltd; Figure 11.23 © Roland DG; Figure 11.28 GoodMood Photo – Fotolia; Figure 11.30 © Crown copyright material is reproduced with the permission of the Controller of HMSO and Queen's Printer for Scotland; Figure 11.31 © centauria/iStockphoto.com; Figure 11.35 Albert Lozano-Nieto – Fotolia; Figure 11.36 Andrzej Tokarski – Fotolia

All other photographs in this volume are supplied by the authors.

Illustrations by Barking Dog Art.

Every effort has been made to trace and acknowledge the ownership of copyright. The publishers will be happy to make arrangements with any copyright owners that it has not been possible to contact.

Contents

chapter 1
Properties of materials

Learning objectives

By the end of this section you should have developed a knowledge and understanding of:

- the working characteristics of paper, board and other graphic materials
- the units by which the thickness of paper and board are measured
- paper sizes A0 to A6 and their relationship to each other
- the properties and uses of different types of new, recycled and reusable paper and board
- how paper-based boards can be laminated to other materials and the composite adjusted to create different properties for specific purposes
- how plastics have different properties and can be used in different ways
- the names of thermoplastics and be able to select an appropriate material
- how and why block modelling fits into the design cycle
- the purpose of models
- basic modelling materials and properties
- block models and their advantages
- types of plastics and their manufacturing properties
- reasons for choosing specific plastics
- smart materials and their properties
- different types of modern materials
- available alternatives to thermoplastics.

Introduction

For designing and making, there is a large range of materials available for the graphic designer. Prototypes, models and mock-ups can be constructed using a combination of traditional paper, card and board media. Materials can be combined, shaped and blended to share the designer's exciting graphical ideas with other people.

Specific materials are chosen to perform certain functions. For example, solid whiteboard card is lightweight, relatively strong and can be easily printed upon. These features make it a cost-effective method of packing all types of products. This chapter will explore different types of materials and their uses. You will need to understand the properties of a variety of materials, and give reasons why you would choose these to use in your own design projects. Material specifications and choice are an important part of a designer's role.

1.1 Classification of graphic materials

△ **Figure 1.1** Poster graphic used to advertise music event

The characteristics of paper, board and other graphic materials

Paper is manufactured by squeezing the fibres of damp, fibrous materials and then drying them to form sheets of paper. The better the material, the more care with the pressing of the fibres and the greater accuracy of drying, the better the quality and thickness of the paper. Paper is one of the more common materials used by graphic designers. Papers are produced for various purposes, and they differ in weight and size.

The weight of paper is measured in grams per square metre, known as **gsm**. Card and board are measured in a different unit, called microns.

Thicker heavy-duty paper-based material is usually described as card and board when it exceeds 200 gsm. Card and boards can be produced in ideal thicknesses for the products (such as for packaging).

The most widely used size of drawing sheets is the A series. A0 has an area of one square metre, and each size halves as the series of sizes progresses. The relationship is that A0 is double the size of A1; A1 is double A2; down to A5 being double the size of A6.

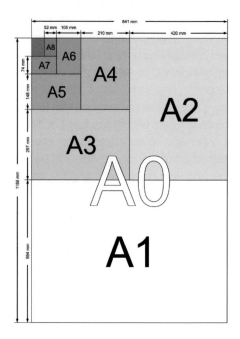

△ **Figure 1.2** Paper size relationship

Paper can be manufactured to give the material different properties for a range of uses – such as high quality gloss-finished paper used for photographs, or the thinner newsprint paper that is absorbent, cheap and of low quality. There are many ways to change the properties of paper and card, but the three main ways are:

1. **Laminating:** the gluing together of layers (plies) of card or paper to achieve a board that will meet the designer's needs. A range of laminated boards is manufactured.

2. **Coating:** china clay or chalk can be sprayed onto the surface to give a smooth finish.

3. **Sizing:** the paper or card is sealed by a chemical agent to improve its ability to accept ink. The sizing can affect the whiteness (brightness) of the material surface.

The graphic designer can add further

modifications, and give additional properties to the products by using boards made of synthetic materials (such as foam boards, corriflute).

> ## Key point
> Paper is made by squeezing together damp, fibrous material which is dried to form paper.

Exam practice question

What units are used when buying card and board?

Paper

Paper is produced to meet many different graphical needs. A newspaper requires a paper that can withstand the high-speed printing process, whereas a menu requires a paper that offers colour and texture. The graphic designer works with paper that can be bought in many finishes, different sizes and weights. Basic types are:

o virgin fibre paper, which has never been used before to make paper or other products

o recycled paper: printed or unprinted wastepaper collected from offices or households, which contains a minimum of 75 per cent genuine waste.

△ **Figure 1.3** Paper

> ## Key term
>
> **gsm** – grams per square metre.

General-purpose paper for everyday use has a weight of 80 gsm. For business and home use, paper is readily available in standard sizes and is inexpensive when bought in bulk. It is used for writing, sketching, photocopying or computer printing in the home.

Vast amounts of paper are consumed in the industrial printing process, with the customer deciding on the quality of paper used in the process. Using sheets in a standard size will always reduce the cost of paper to the customer.

There is an enormous choice in the types of paper used in graphic design, which can be purchased in a wide range of colours, coatings, textures and sizes.

Cartridge paper

Cartridge paper is often used for graphic design. It is thicker than ordinary paper and weighs between 120 and 150 gsm. It is made from chemical wood pulps, espartos or both. The texture is rough, semi-rough or smooth, depending on its use. It is named for its original use: the wrapping of ball and powder for muskets. The most common use for cartridge paper is for illustrating. Cartridge paper is well suited for use with paints, oil pastels, pencils or chalk to create graphics on the thick, textured paper.

Many brochures, pamphlets and booklets are printed with cartridge paper. Pamphlets fold well when made with cartridge paper of a thicker weight. Logos and initials can be pressed or embossed into the paper. Cartridge paper is an excellent paper for general purposes.

Layout paper

Layout paper is a strong, heavyweight paper with a smooth finish and a degree of transparency that is used in the preparation of a product layout; also called tissue overlay, the paper weighs about 50 gsm and is inexpensive to buy. Due to its translucent appearance, a drawing can be traced, allowing a quick and easy transfer of images that can be modified and developed.

Layout paper is used as an overlay by the graphic designer to trace accepted elements on the design. As new elements are approved or accepted, the designer can retrace them onto new layout paper, until eventually the layout is complete.

Bleedproof paper

Bleedproof paper is used for high-quality presentations and writing paper. Drawing on the front produces clean, crisp lines. The paper has the ability to absorb and hold inks and water-based paints. It is especially effective when used with felt markers. Bleedproof paper is moderately expensive to buy, and is produced in weights of between 120 and 150 gsm.

Tracing paper

Tracing paper is named because a graphic designer can easily trace an image onto it. When tracing paper is placed onto a picture, the picture is easily viewable through the tracing paper. Thus, it becomes easy for the designer to find edges in the picture and trace the image onto the tracing paper.

The recommended media for tracing paper are generally listed as pencil, pen and markers. The greater the weight of tracing paper (it can be between 40 and 90 gsm), then the more expensive to buy.

> ### Key point
> Use the paper designed for the job.

> ### Exam tip
> Exam questions may ask what paper you would use when using markers.

> ### Exam practice question
> When choosing paper to do a presentation drawing for a client, give reasons for your choice of paper.

Cardboard

Cardboard is available in sheets of different sizes, thickness and finish. The term 'card' tends to refer to thinner material (as used for greetings cards), while the term 'cardboard' refers to thicker material (as used to mount prints). Corrugated card is also available in rolls and sheets.

Cardboard products can be recycled as long as they are not laminated with another material. The fibres that make up cardboard become shorter every time they are pulped, which means that cardboard can be recycled only four or five times before the fibres disintegrate.

The thickness of card and cardboard is usually measured in microns (1,000 microns = 1 mm). Cardboard is usually over 1,000 microns in thickness. The card used in graphics usually ranges from around 200 microns to 1,000 microns. Card is sometimes described in terms of how many sheets of paper thick it is; for example, a 240 micron card may be known as '3-sheet'.

Card and cardboard are available in a variety of different colours, finishes and textures and can be classified as:

◁ **Figure 1.4**
Cardboard

○ **Corrugated cardboard**, which is often used in packaging
○ **Flat cardboard**, which is used to make products such as cereal packets.

When buying cardboard you must remember that it can be expensive, so you must choose the correct size and thickness to avoid wastage.

Corrugated cardboard

The board is made from papers made up from cellulose fibres, which are virgin or recycled. Corrugated board is made from a combination of two sheets of paper called **liners**, glued to a corrugated inner medium called the **fluting**.

Corrugated cardboard packaging is a versatile, light, robust, economic and practical form of packaging. The products made from corrugated cardboard use a natural, environmentally friendly material with a good record for recycling and recovery.

Corrugated cardboard offers the graphic designer almost unlimited possible combinations of board types, flute sizes, paper weights, adhesive types, treatments and coatings. The designer can use the material for making simple or complex boxes, and also use the cardboard's structures to protect a product.

As a material, corrugated board is inexpensive to buy, and versatile for design and manufacture.

Mounting board

Mounting board is an incredibly useful and versatile board which is excellent for picture mounting, framing and model-making. It is stiff but lightweight, and easy to cut with a sharp craft knife.

Mounting board is perfect for framing presentations and display. The mounting board comprises three basic components: the surface paper, core and backing paper. The core and the backing paper contain alkaline fillers to enhance their useful lifespan by minimising the effect of atmospheric pollutants.

The board is expensive and can be purchased in a variety of thicknesses (from 1,000 to 1,500 microns) and colours.

Duplex board

This kind of board is used for food packaging and carton manufacturing. It can be used for containers and can contain liquids as it may have a waterproof liner on the inside. It can have a wax feel.

Duplex board is used by the food industry, and consequently recycled card is not used in its manufacture. It is constructed of multiple ply, which provides it with good strength for weights between 230 and 420 gsm.

Various coatings can be applied to provide a surface suitable for printing. Textured ply can be used to allow the designer to enhance the packaging.

Solid whiteboard

Whiteboard is normally top-quality cardboard made from quality bleached wood pulp. It is the best card for printing on to, and consequently it is used for point of sale, frozen food, cosmetics packaging, hardback books and products which require an excellent surface.

The quality of the card means that designers usually keep it for more expensive graphics products.

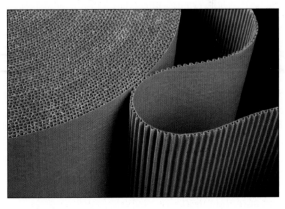

△ **Figure 1.5** Corrugated cardboard

Greyboard

Greyboard is produced from 100 per cent recycled fibre, which is biodegradable over six months. The board offers a smooth surface and high bulk-to-weight ratio; this makes it useful for thick but lightweight uses. Good grades of greyboard are flat. They have a cross-grain, making the board strong and tough in all directions.

Greyboard is not normally visible as it is covered on both sides by a material chosen to suit the design. The board is suitable for screen printing, paper-onto-board lamination, and used for ring binders, files, slip cases, wallets, bookbinding, picture mounting and jigsaws.

Cartonboard

Cardboards can be described as cartonboards and are mainly used in the packaging industries. They can be treated or laminated to give the card specific and additional qualities.

○ Solid bleached board (SBB) is regarded as the highest quality packaging, with a white printable surface. It is used for perfume, chocolates and cigars.
○ Solid unbleached board (SUB) is usually brown and needs to be strong because it is used in the drinks industry.
○ Folding box board (FBB) has a white or printed top layer with a darker bottom layer. It is used for printing on for toy and games packaging.
○ White lined chipboard (WLC) has a white top surface that allows printing, and is made from recycled board. It is used to package soap powders and detergents.

Some of the coatings on the cartonboard make the material more difficult to recycle; for example:

○ Plastic coating: used for water resistance. Drinks' cartons use the coating to stop the liquid contained from soaking into the material.
○ Aluminium foil: for food products to give a bacterial barrier against possible contamination.
○ Greaseproof: used for muffins and cup cakes, it is structural while cooking.
○ Wax coating: used for drinks' containers such as those found in fast-food outlets.

Foam board

Foam board is a lightweight board made from polystyrene sandwiched between sheets of paper or card. Foam board is usually white, but other colours, including black, are available. It is available in a variety of sheet sizes, thicknesses and colours. The most common sheet sizes are A2 to A3. Common thicknesses of foam board sheet are between 3 mm and 10 mm, with perhaps 5 mm the most commonly used.

Foam board is commonly used for display work and model-making. You should always test an adhesive before using it on foam board, as some adhesives contain polystyrene solvents, which will melt polystyrene.

The board will cut with a clean edge when a sharp craft knife is used.

Plastic sheet and sections

Plastic is a general term for a wide range of synthetic materials made from oil. Plastics can be thermoset (cannot be reworked), or thermo (can be reheated and reworked). The graphic designer can purchase the plastics in many different types, colours and forms (such as sheet, block, section, rod and tube). A good model-making supplier will have a wide range of sizes available. A section is a shaped strip of material (for example, a U section or an L section).

The most common types of plastic used in graphics are high-impact polystyrene (HIPS), polyvinyl chloride (PVC), polypropylene, acrylic and self-adhesive vinyl.

○ Rigid plastics are ideal for model-making and can be shaped and joined with the correct tools and adhesives.
○ Flexible plastics such as the self-adhesive vinyl can be laminated to the card, or cut into lettering, symbols and shapes to enhance the graphic designer's products.

○ Plastic sheet can be placed in layers with different cards, papers and plastics to form a composite material. The composite material may have the combined quality characteristics of all the materials used.

Corriflute

Corriflute or correx is an extruded corrugated plastic sheet produced from high-impact polypropylene resin. It is a lightweight material, which can easily be cut with a sharp craft knife.

Corriflute is available in sheets of different sizes, thickness and colour. The most common sheet size is 610 mm x 610 mm. The most common thickness for corriflute sheet is 4 mm. Corriflute is usually purchased in packs of mixed colours that contain red, blue, white, yellow, green and black sheets.

Corriflute is commonly used to create signs, such as those used by estate agents, and for constructing plastic containers and packaging. Corriflute can be recycled and is therefore considered by many to be environmentally friendly.

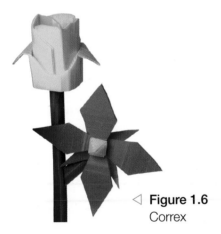

◁ **Figure 1.6**
Correx

StyroFoam™

Styrofoam™ is a general term for expanded polystyrene foam. Styrofoam has a small, closed cell structure which gives a smooth, fine surface that is stable, easily shaped and emits no odour. It does not absorb water and can be cut, sawn and sanded.

Excellent shaping can be done with a hot wire carving tool at a low heat and in a well-ventilated room. It is ideal for modelling because of its incredible versatility.

Styrofoam™ is available in a wide range of sheets and blocks, and is often used in packaging and modelling. It comes in sheets and blocks of different sizes and thickness. A common sheet size is 600 mm x 1,200 mm, with thicknesses between 25 mm and 100 mm.

The colour is either pale blue or pink, but this is unimportant because Styrofoam™ is often painted after shaping. If you are using Styrofoam™ to make a concept model, you can reduce waste by gluing offcuts together to make the correct-size block.

△ **Figure 1.7** Styrofoam™

Key points

The main materials used in graphics are:

○ paper
○ cardboard
○ plastic sheet and sections
○ corriflute
○ Styrofoam™.

Exam tip

The best way of developing a good working knowledge of the range of materials used in graphics is to use them in your designing and making tasks.

Key term
Composite – paper-based boards are laminated to other materials and the board can be adjusted to create different properties for specific purposes.

1.2 **Making judgements about material properties**

The functionality of a material can be described using its properties. Properties are the characteristics of a material's performance, look and use. When choosing a material, knowing how the material will perform is often a good starting point.

Designers use terms to describe the properties of materials when specifying their needs. In some cases, the terms are different from what we might use every day. A boxer is described as hard or tough; this would mean the same thing. However, when used as a description of material properties these have different meanings.

Physical properties
Hardness

A hard material will not dent or scratch easily. Acrylic is a hard material; foam board is not.

◁ **Figure 1.8** Glass is optically very clear and does not scratch when cleaned, but can shatter

Toughness

Toughness is the ability of a material to absorb physical impact without permanently deforming. Polycarbonate, used to make riot shields, is tough as it will take blows from thrown objects without breaking (see section 1.3 below for more information on this). Glass is hard as it is not easily scratched. However, glass is not tough as it shatters easily.

Strength

A material with good strength will hold its shape under load. A strong material will not deform when pressure is applied. Strong materials are often difficult to cut and form. A formed writing tablet in a bank could be manufactured from ABS. ABS would not deform when being used as a rest for writing.

Strength is dependent upon the type of load that is applied to it.

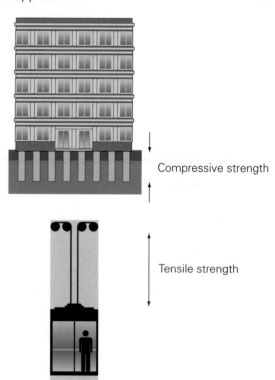

Compressive strength

Tensile strength

△ **Figure 1.9** The strength of a material can be judged in different ways

- ○ **Tensile** loads are stretching loads. A thin wire is difficult to break when it is stretched. However, if you were to squash the wire it would deform, so it would have a poor **compressive** strength.
- ○ **Shear** loads are cutting loads, like using scissors. Forces are applied at one point on the material from two different directions.
- ○ **Rotational** strength is a guide to how well a material will resist a twisting load.

Flexibility

A flexible material will be soft and movable. Banners and flags are made from flexible material; they can move and be wrapped around items. Thin acetate can be bent easily to form a window in a piece of packaging.

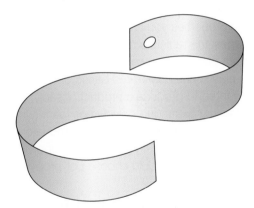

△ **Figure 1.10** Flexibility

Rigidity

Rigidity is the opposite of flexibility. Rigid materials are stiff and do not bend or flex under their own weight. Materials that have a level of rigidity are useful for forming structural items. Foam board is quite rigid and is ideal for forming walls in architectural models.

Ductility

A ductile material will be easy to form and change shape.

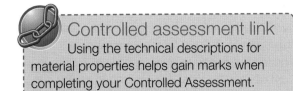

Controlled assessment link
Using the technical descriptions for material properties helps gain marks when completing your Controlled Assessment.

Elasticity

Elasticity is the ability of a material to return to its original shape when the applied load has been removed.

Plasticity

A plastic product will stay in the shape that it has been moved to after the load has been removed.

Conductivity

Conductive materials allow heat or electricity to flow through them. It is usual to specify which conductivity is being talked about, either thermal or electrical.

Weight

In a graphic product a designer should consider the weight of material. A sign could be chosen because it is light, like a corriflute 'house for sale' sign; or a wooden base may be used on a point of sale to give ballast to help the product stay upright.

Often the strength-to-weight ratio is considered. The designer would try to get the best compromise between how strong a material is against its weight. Aluminium has a good strength-to-weight ratio. It is relatively strong for the weight of the material. This is important, for example, in large motorway signs.

Colour

Some materials have a colour built into them. If you were to cut red acrylic, it would be red all the way through the section. This is a useful quality if the piece is to be machined or sanded and polished, and the same colour is required on the whole surface.

Acrylic is one of the many plastics that can be purchased in a range of colours. It can also be **transparent** or semi-transparent (**opaque**). The level of opacity can be specified. A 50 per cent opaque material is ideal for illuminated shop signs; the colour will shine out brightly at night to attract the attention of passing customers.

In signage, a material called **engraving laminate** is often used. This has layers of different-coloured plastic laminated together. The first layer is machined away to leave the second colour visible. This technique is commonly seen on interior door signs.

Non-physical properties

Alongside the physical properties of the material, the design can also consider the material's non-physical properties. These include the available finish, environmental issues and cost.

Finish

Finish is the final surface decoration or technique on a product or item. Coloured plastics that are vacuum formed tend to be self-finishing. The quality in which they leave the mould is how they will be presented to the customer or client. If a blemish appears on the surface, the product can be **finished** by polishing.

○ A finish could be paint, varnish, stain or dye.
○ A finishing technique could be sanding, filing, polishing.

A texture can be applied to a mould for injection moulding; the texture is a finish. A change of texture on the surface of a product is a good way of indicating a change of function or purpose; as well as adding a visual aesthetic, a handle on a glue gun can be textured to help grip and indicate the correct position to hold the tool.

Activity
List the ways in which a finish could be matt, satin, glossy or reflective.

Environmental and sustainability issues

A material can be chosen for its positive effect on the environment. A positive quality of a material is the ease with which can be recycled, or whether it is sourced from a sustainable outlet.

Cost

It may sometimes be necessary to choose a material for a particular product based on its cost. Some materials are more expensive to buy than others and you may, for example, need to choose a cheaper material in order to keep to a budget.

It is important to have an understanding of each of these material properties so that you can make judgements about materials and select the most appropriate material to use based on the properties you are looking for. Table 1.1 on pages 11–13 lists a range of properties of different plastics. You can see, for example, that each plastic has been rated based on its cost. If you wanted to produce a product cheaply, you might select expanded polystyrene foam (which is relatively cheap) instead of polycarbonate (which is expensive). If you wanted your product to be flexible, you would choose polypropylene.

1.3 **Understand the properties and uses of thermoplastics**

Plastics belong to two families: **thermoplastic** plastic and **thermoset** plastic. Thermoplastics will soften when heated, allowing the shape to be changed through forming; thermoset plastic cannot be reformed.

Plastics are not necessarily cheap. They are a complex blend of chemicals that give the material different properties. Additives are often used in plastics to increase a specific performance, change the colour or feel. A downside to additives is that they can cause a negative side effect. For example, polycarbonate, used on police riot shields, is almost unbreakable. A riot shield will be able to withstand a sledgehammer being smashed against it. So why is it not used in everyday glazing? The reason is not the cost, but because it is very easily scratched, making it difficult to clean and keep optically perfect.

is used; perspex, manufactured by ICI is polymethyl methacrylate, also known as acrylic.

Exam tip

In the exam you will only need to specify the initials of these chemicals.

Activity

Think of your kitchen at home. Make a list of everything that is made out of plastic. (Do not forget what is stored inside the cupboards and the fridge.)

Draw a plan view of your kitchen. Mark each piece of plastic with a little dot. Some areas will probably have many more dots than others.

◁ **Figure 1.11** Riot shields withstand impact, but polycarbonate is easily scratched

The chemicals that make up a plastic are often used as its name. These can be very long, so usually they are abbreviated; for example, acrylonitrile butadiene styrene is shortened to ABS. Sometimes the manufacturer's name

What is a property?

How a material performs is called its **properties**. A material's property will describe what the material will do; it is the character of the material. As a designer it is important to know what the material's properties are, and to understand the terminology that is used to describe them.

Name	Chemical name	Abbreviation/ name	Recycling symbol	Properties	Uses	Process	Stock forms	Cost 1–5 (5=high)
Low-density polythene	Low-density polyethylene	Ldpe		Wide range of colours; good electrical insulator; good chemical resistance; soft waxy plastic	Plastic sacks, toys	Extruded, injection moulded	Powder granules, sheet, film	3
High-density polythene	High-density polyethylene	Hdpe		Can be sterilised; range of colours; soft material	Buckets, bowls, milk crates	Extruded, injection moulded	Powder, granules, sheet, film	3
PVC	Poly vinyl chloride	PVC	3	Range of colours; exterior use; tough, hard plastic	Pipes and gutters, flooring	Extruded, injection forming and vacuum forming	Powder, granules, extrusions and sheet	3

△ **Table 1.1** Properties of different plastics

Cont.

11

Name	Chemical name	Abbreviation/ name	Recycling symbol	Properties	Uses	Process	Stock forms	Cost 1–5 (5=high)
Acrylic (Perspex)	Polymethyl methacrylate	Perspex acrylic		Optically clear; hard material; variety of colours; durable; easily polished; weather resistant	Signs, aircraft canopies, baths,	Injection, extrusion, vacuum forming	Sheet, rod, tube	4
High-impact polystyrene	High-impact polystyrene	HIPs	6	Can be clear; lightweight; rigid	Models, cups	Extruded, injection moulding, vacuum forming	Sheet, granules	2
Acrylonitrile butadiene styrene	Acrylonitrile butadiene styrene	ABS		A strong, heat-resistant plastic; can take a rigid form	Kettles, hairdryers, casing of many small products	Extruded, injection moulding, vacuum forming	Sheet, granules	4
Polymide	Polymide	Nylon		Resilient; hard-wearing; self-lubricating	Gears, bearings, combs	Extruded injection moulded	Sheet, tube, rod, granules	4
Bioplastic				Biodegradable; starch based	Food packaging	Vacuum formed	Sheet, film	4
PET	Polyethylene terephthalate	PET	1	Cost effective	Bottles	Blow moulding, vacuum forming	Granules	1
Polystyrene		PS	6	Good forming; hard and rigid	CD cases, yoghurt pots	Vacuum forming, injection moulding	Granules, sheet	2
Expanded polystyrene foam		Styrofoam	3	Lightweight; impact resistant	Protective infill packaging, models	Foam injected		1
Polypropylene		PP	5	Flexible; scratch resistant; low friction	Cutting boards, crisp packets	Injection moulded	Film, sheet, granules	3

△ **Table 1.1** Properties of different plastics

Cont.

Name	Chemical name	Abbreviation/ name	Recycling symbol	Properties	Uses	Process	Stock forms	Cost 1–5 (5=high)
Polycarbonate				Impact resistant; easily scratched	Riot shields, safety goggles	Extrusion, injection moulded, vacuum formed after drying	Sheet, granules, film	5

△ **Table 1.1** Properties of different plastics

Thermoplastics are used regularly in graphic products. Vacuum-formed food-grade thermoplastics are used to form clear containers for shop-bought sandwiches. PVC bubbles allow the buyer to see the product, while protecting it from damage.

Activity

Advent calendars are popular at Christmas. Behind the doors, the chocolates are often shaped into festive shapes. These treats can be held in shape by a vacuum-formed tray, which positions the chocolate so that the pieces line up with the doors.

Design a vacuum-formed tray for the last five days of Christmas. Remember that behind the door marked the 24th, the sweet is usually extra special!

1.4 Understanding the use of sheet and block modelling materials

Block modelling is an important part of a designer's toolkit. It supports sketching and allows ideas to be considered in a quick format. Modelling in 3D allows the form of the product to be observed from all angles. Proportion and user viewpoints can be evaluated and developed further.

It is a good idea to photograph block models. These can be used on your development sheets in your folder. Draw over them, making notes to show what changes you would make on the strength of the models being made.

Several materials are used to manufacture block models. Usually they are lightweight, quick, and easily adhered to; for example:

○ foam core board
○ corrugated plastic
○ expanded PVC
○ Styrofoam™; expanded polystyrene
○ clay
○ card
○ paper.

The creation of the test model is to help develop the product form, not to be a realistic version of the outcome.

△ **Figure 1.12** Clay used as a block model

13

Sheet and block modelling

Modelling is a key part of a designer's work. It is particularly important if working in a 3D form or space. Interior designers model how a room will look. With a small camera and fibre optics, they can quickly 'walk through' the room to get a feel of how the finished space will look.

Architectural models are often made from foam board (see section 1.1). Foam board is a thin foam sandwiched between lightweight card. It is clean and easy to use, ideal for sharp, crisp straight edges. Joining is possible with PVA or double-sided tape; corners and folds are a little tricky and would need to be V-scored to give an accurate fold.

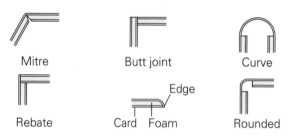

| Mitre | Butt joint | Curve |
| Rebate | Card   Foam (Edge) | Rounded |

△ **Figure 1.13** The lightweight foam board can be constructed in several ways

Block modelling process

Sketch modelling

Product designers will make several 3D **sketch models** before producing the final design. Sketch modelling is very important to the design process. Models can be used to help develop the design, or test part of the design, as well as representing the finished article. During the design process, it is important at an early stage for a quick, 3D representation to be made, as this will help you to see where problems might occur.

These models could be made out of a wide range of materials, such as paper, card or foam. Foam models can give a quick accurate presentation of form.

Realisation model

The final **realisation model** can be made to scale and should closely represent the final product. A professional designer will take this final model and his visualisation boards to the client to show in detail how the product would look and feel.

Figure 1.14 shows a high-quality realisation model. It is not a real camping stove, but has been made from cibatool and finished with acrylic spray paint to represent the final product.

△ **Figure 1.14** Realisation models give a realistic representation of the final form, and are produced after the development is complete.

Properties of sheet and block modelling materials

Material	Type of Model	Tools	Finishing	Advantages	Disadvantages
Balsa wood	Sketch model, architectural and framework models	Light-duty woodworking tools	Sanding, filler, paint	Easily glued, lightweight, easily worked, sustainable product	Expensive, not so strong along the grain
MDF	Realisation model, useful for vacuum-formed moulds, and finished handheld models	Woodworking equipment, CNC router	Sanding, primer, spray paint	Quite easy to work, cost-effective, readily available, can be CNC-routed	Produces dust, heavy, difficult to achieve fine detail in the final product
Plasticine or clay	Sketch model, ergonomic testing, quick moulding of complex shapes	Hand and shaping tools	Hand-smoothed, clay can be sanded when dry	Dry clay can be vacuum formed, easily reused	Quality of finish
Expanded polystyrene foam	Sketch model, shaped models of the final design	Hot wire, saws, files, sandpaper	Sand, filler and paint	Lightweight, very easy and quick to work	Quality of finish, not recyclable
Card	Sketch model, realisation model, packaging, pop ups	Scissors, craft knives, laser, CNC blade cutter, die cutter	Paint, vinyl stickers, airbrush	Readily available, lightweight, graphics easily applied, can be recycled	Difficult to produce clean curves
Modelling card/ mounting board	Sketch model, architectural presentation model, book covers	Scissors, craft knives, laser, CNC blade cutter	Paint, vinyl stickers, airbrush	Rigid to use, quite easily cut, variety of base colours, can be recycled	Harder to fold and use than the lighter card

△ **Table 1.2** Properties of sheet and block modelling materials

Cont.

Material	Type of Model	Tools	Finishing	Advantages	Disadvantages
Corrugated card	Sketch model, quick architectural models, strong packaging mock ups	Scissors, craft knives, laser, CNC blade cutter	Paint, vinyl stickers, airbrush	Readily available, easy to cut, can be recycled	Weak along the flutes, uneven edges after cutting
Closed cell polyethylene foam (Plastazote)	Sketch model, flat models, interlaced shapes	Scissors, craft knives, laser, die cutter	Self finishing	Colourful selection, flexible easily worked and cut	Limited to set colours, quite expensive, not recyclable
Polymorph	Sketch model, ergonomic testing, trial injection moulding	Hand sculpted, light woodworking tools when solid	Sanded when hard, primed and spray painted	Mouldable when warm, can be traditionally worked when solid, reheat to reuse	Expensive
Corrugated Plastic	Sketch model, point-of-sale displays	Scissors, craft knives	Vinyl stickers	Lightweight, easy to cut	Weak along the flutes, uneven edges after cutting
Acetate	Visual opening on packaging	Scissors, craft knives, laser, CNC blade cutter	Vinyl stickers	Easy to cut, optically clear	Expensive, hard to colour, not recyclable
Acrylic sheet (perspex) and rod	Block and realisation, windows in architectural models.	Light woodworking tools and machinery, laser cutter, polish, thermoformed	Self-finished, can be polished	Clear or a range of colours, excellent quality of finish, can be recycled	Expensive
Foam board	Block model, architectural and POS model	Craft knives, laser cutter	Vinyl stickers, adhered images	Lightweight, easily cut	Can be squashed and bent, difficult to cut complex shapes, not recyclable

△ **Table 1.2** Properties of sheet and block modelling materials

Cont.

Material	Type of Model	Tools	Finishing	Advantages	Disadvantages
Cibatool	Realisation model, for models that are to be painted	Wood working tools, CNC router	Sanded, primed and sprayed	Very good surface finish, can be CNC routed	Very expensive, not recyclable
ABS (Rapid prototype)	Realisation model, small accurate finished products	Rapid prototype	Sanded, primed and sprayed	Incredible accuracy, one-stop shaping, can be recycled	Very expensive material and capital cost

△ **Table 1.2** Properties of sheet and block modelling materials

1.5 Finishes

The type of finish which you apply to your model depends upon what you want the model to do, and how the model is to be used. If you are testing strength, a beautiful painted finish is probably unnecessary; if the model is used as a final realisation or a presentation of the final design to a client, then the quality, care, attention to detail and finish application are very important.

Thermoplastics can be self-finishing, so painting and priming are not always necessary. However if the plastic is to be vacuum formed, the surface quality of the forming mould is important and will need to be sanded with a fine glass paper. Any bump or blemish on the mould will be seen in the final piece.

Glass paper, emery cloths and wet and dry abrasive sheets have various grades of roughness. A number is given to highlight how rough the grit on the paper is; the higher the number the finer the grain, and the smoother the surface of your work.

The edges of acrylic can be polished by flame or toothpaste. Toothpaste can be used as a form of abrasive paste. Commercial abrasive pastes also have a variety of roughness; these are used extensively in the jewellery industry.

Activity

Collect small squares of the different grades and types of abrasive paper. Place these in your workbook in order of roughness.

Finishes for modelling material

Sanding sealer

Sealing a porous surface is necessary if the model is to be painted or lacquered. Commercial sealants are available for a variety of materials, including wood and foam.

Primer

Primer is a basecoat of paint which acts as a strong, even adhesive for the paint. Primer will help the colour of the applied paint to be even, and keys the paint to the surface (**key** is the technical name for helping the paint stick).

Cellulose paint

Most spray paints are cellulose paints. Often these are not allowed to be used in schools. Spraying must take place in a well-ventilated or air-extracted area. The paint should be applied evenly in light coats that build up to give an even, run-free finish.

Emulsion paint

Emulsion paint can be applied by spray gun, roller or brush. A very smooth finish is difficult to achieve with a brush. White emulsion is often used as a sealant on MDF.

Emulsion is water-based and can be applied to foam block models. It is not aggressive and will not melt the foam. The surface finish will be poor but it will represent blocks of colour.

Varnish

Acrylic, water-based varnish will apply a gloss, satin or matt finish to wood. Usually applied with a brush, two or three layers are necessary to give a smooth, even finish. Varnish gives a protective layer to the wood.

Wood stains

These do not protect the wood from scratches, but will allow a change of colour to the wood used. For example: a cheap pine model can be stained to look like expensive, strong oak.

Polish

Polishes and paste are used to remove scratches from the surface of metals and plastics. Surfaces can be burnished to a mirror finish with a fine paste.

Using adhesives

Often models are constructed from different materials and parts, which will be assembled together. Adhesives are a good method of quickly fixing parts together. The adhesion can be permanent or a light, removable fix.

Tensol

Tensol is a cement for fixing acrylic to acrylic. It chemically melts the acrylic surfaces together as a weld.

Epoxy resin

Usually this is a two-part mix and is used for joining parts that are made from different materials together. It can be used on metals, woods and some plastics.

PVA

This glue gives a strong fix between timber-based products, both man-made and natural.

Superglue

Most materials will adhere together with superglue, including joining dissimilar materials together.

Hot glue gun

This is a quick way of fixing different materials together. The disadvantage is that it tends to be applied as a thick strand between layers. This can be an unwanted visible blemish on visible surfaces.

Double-sided tape

This can be used as a quick fixing of most materials. The strength of the bond varies between different brands of tape. It can be used as a temporary or permanent fixing.

Key terms

Key – helping the paint to stick to a surface.

Permanent fixing – this is so strong that in order to break the bond, the material itself is damaged.

Temporary fixing – can be reused or removed without damage to the original part.

1.6 **Smart and modern materials**

Smart materials

Smart materials are a range of materials that will change their property when exposed to an outside influence. It could be said that smart materials are very clever. This influence could be heat, light, pressure, electricity, moisture or magnets. Usually, the material reverts back to its original state after the exposure has been removed.

Most of the types of smart materials are preceded by a Latin or Greek word which gives a clue as to what they do:

○ **Photo**-sensitive material reacts to light.
○ **Thermo**-sensitive material reacts to heat.
○ **Hydro**-sensitive material reacts to water or moisture.
○ **Pies**-sensitive (the Greek word for squeeze or press) reacts to pressure.
○ **Electro**-sensitive materials react to electricity.

Smart materials within graphic products are mostly used in inks and printing.

Photo-chromatic

Materials and inks which are photo-chromatic change colour depending upon the amount of light that falls upon them. Light-sensitive sunglasses are an obvious example.

△ **Figure 1.15** Photo-chromatic sunglasses change according to the amount of light upon them

Thermo-chromatic

Thermo-chromatic materials alter their colour depending upon temperature. These have been used in a variety of graphic products from T-shirts to children's thermometers. Thermo-chromatic inks can be printed onto many different materials textiles, tiles, card and plastic. Some bottle labels turn blue to show that they have been chilled enough in the refrigerator.

A mug can change colour as hot water is added to it. The mug shown in Figure 1.16 changes the shape of the map to illustrate how the countries would look if sea levels rise and countries lose their landmass through global warming.

△ **Figure 1.16** A thermo-chromatic mug

Blending different thermo-chromatic inks allow inks to react to different temperatures. This facility is commonly used in strip thermometers. A strip is applied to the skin which reacts accurately to degree rises in body temperature.

Hydro-chromatic inks

Inks which are hydro-chromatic change colour as they dry out. This can be used in a variety of areas; one fun way is an umbrella that changes colour when wet. They can also be used as indicators of when potted plants need watering.

Activity

Design a T-shirt for your summer holidays that uses photo-chromatic inks. Which areas could change or appear as you bask in the sun?

Shape Memory Alloys (SMAs)

Materials made from SMAs will return to their original shape when an electric current is passed through them. This process is used in the telecoms industry: small individual cables can be batched together, and then an SMA ring is placed over them. When the current is passed, the ring returns to a smaller size, clamping the individual cables together.

Polymorph

Polymorph is a material that gels and softens at 62 degrees Centigrade. It is usually sold in bead form, which can be poured into warm water. The beads gel and form together to make a material similar to soft plasticine. This can be hand-moulded and formed into a variety of shapes. When it cools, it becomes solid, like a piece of plastic. It is useful to make prototype models and sets rigid enough to be used as a vacuum-forming mould.

When reheated, the polymorph turns back into a soft formable material. It can be reused many times.

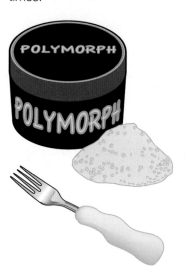

◁ **Figure 1.17** Polymorph granules are mouldable and reusable at 62 degrees Centigrade

Modern materials

New materials are constantly being developed to meet particular functions or needs.

Precious metal clays (PMC)

Precious metal clays were developed in the 1990s. Minute particles of silver or gold are mixed with a binding material that can be moulded like clay. This material is particularly used in the jewellery industry. Complex shapes can be moulded by hand and air dried; they are then heated until the particles of metal melt and fuse together. When cooled, the material looks as though it has been manufactured from a pure precious metal.

Cornstarch polymers

One of the first companies to use cornstarch polymers was Cadbury's, who used them to make the inner tray to hold chocolates in its Milk Tray range. Cornstarch polymers can be vacuum formed, and act like a thermoplastic. However, when immersed in water they will completely biodegrade. Starch from potatoes, corn and maize is used to replace the oil-based product in traditional thermoplastics.

Paperfoam

Paperfoam is a material made from natural fibres and potato starch. It is shaped in an injection moulding process and can be used to make products such as CD or DVD packaging, as well as packaging for consumer electronics. It is lightweight, strong and fully biodegradable. Its manufacture causes a fraction of the carbon dioxide emissions (85 per cent lower) of an equivalent thermoplastic component.

△ **Figure 1.18** Paperfoam can be used as a versatile packaging material

Potatopak

Potatopak is a very eco-friendly product. The industrial food industry uses vast quantities of potatoes to make crisps and chips. During the washing process, starch is leached from the vegetable; this is filtered from the used water, and gives two useful products – clean water and the starch. The starch is placed between moulds, pressurised and heated until it takes the shape of the mould. A process similar to thermoforming plastic can produce similar products, such as plates, packaging trays and cups.

These products are biodegradable and can even be used as pig food.

Activity

Make a photo-rich poster of products that use inserts and internal shaped packing. Identify all those that could be changed to paperfoam or cornstarch polymers.

Other useful resources

The Confederation of Paper Industries (CPI) is the leading organisation working on behalf of the UK paper-related industry. CPI represents the paper chain from the recovery of used paper through papermaking and conversion to distribution. See their website: http://www.paper.org.uk

Paper Industry Technical Association (PITA) is an independent, professionally managed organisation and produces the journal *Paper Technology*. PITA has a knowledge base, a free-to-use resource of generic factsheets covering all aspects of paper, board and tissue manufacture. See their website: http://www.pita.co.uk

Summary

o This chapter has explored several types of materials, their properties and their uses.
o Designers make recommendations for materials to be used in a graphic product.
o These choices are often based upon the best compromise between different properties; for example, cost against strength, or weight to rigidity.
o Having a good knowledge of material properties and manufacturing techniques available for the materials is a key skill for a designer.

Learning objectives

By the end of this section you should have developed a knowledge and understanding of:

○ a range of graphic equipment
○ adhesives used for graphics
○ the cutting tools available for making a graphic product
○ the materials and components used for modelling.

Introduction

There is a range of graphic equipment available and that you will use as part of your GCSE Graphics course. This chapter looks at a range of graphic equipment and gives you guidance on how to use it effectively. This includes adhesives, cutting tools and bought-in components.

2.1 Hand-generated images

Although many hand skills and drawing board techniques have been superseded by very good computer software, there is still a requirement for freehand drawing and more formal drawing as part of GCSE Design and Technology.

Graphics equipment

Below is a list of the key pieces of equipment used for graphics. This is not an exhaustive list, nor is it intended as prescriptive.

○ An HB pencil will cope well as a general tool for sketching. The higher the H number, the harder the pencil and the lighter the line tends to be. A 4B pencil is soft and will give a dark line. Some students will find their work becomes dirty or smudged using a softer pencil. Try putting a piece of scrap paper over the work as you progress, if this is the case.
○ A parallel motion drawing board. It is just as accurate to use a T square but tends to take

longer. This certainly makes it easier to draw parallel lines and achieve accurate work.

○ A pair of set squares. These are triangular in shape, and have a right angle at one corner. The two should be a different shape: one should have a 60- and a 30- degree angle in the two remaining corners, and the other a 45 -degrees angle in both of its corners. You will achieve the best results if they are made from a transparent polymer. Using a set square that has a side of at least 200 mm will also make life easier. An adjustable set square can be bought for more complicated work, but they are seldom used in this exam.
○ The rest of the equipment (such as a compass, eraser, rule and coloured pencils) will be the same as you use for other areas of your education. You could use more sophisticated items, although they may be more expensive; for example, a spring compass tends to be more accurate, and gel pens give a strong clean line.

Exam tip

Using a set square in conjunction with a parallel motion board can save time and earn good marks. Students should be familiar with the use of a compass and various radius aids. It is also good to have some practice with coloured pencils and a range of felt pens.

Activity

Draw an equilateral triangle with sides of 100 mm using a parallel motion or T-square, and a 60-degree set square.

Using the technique shown in Figure 2.1, put a radius in each of the corners. One corner is shown completed, with the stages numbered.

Activity

Draw a series of parallel lines (of any length) across the page using a rule and either set square. Bisect the lines using a compass. Join each of the centres to the next one using a radius aid. See Figure 2.3, and also Figure 2.4 for a range of available aids.

△ **Figure 2.3** Bisecting and joining parallel lines

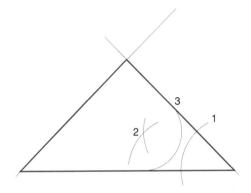

△ **Figure 2.1** An equilateral triangle with radius in one corner

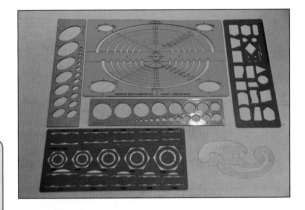

△ **Figure 2.4** Range of available aids

Activity

Using the 45-degree set square, draw a right-angled triangle. Bisect two of the sides using a compass and draw a circle around the triangle from the centre point. See Figure 2.2.

Activity

Using the drawing equipment, make an accurate drawing of a clothes peg. You can complete it either in orthographic or isometric. It might be easier to draw it twice the actual size.

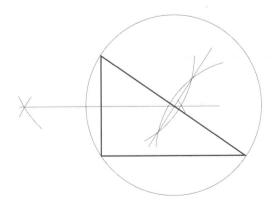

△ **Figure 2.2** Right-angled triangle with circle

2.2 **Adhesives**

Glue	Works on	Description and use
PVA (Polyvinyl acetate)	Foam board, paper, card, wood, leather, canvas	White creamy liquid. Can be diluted and used as a sealant; available in waterproof version. Easy to use although it can wrinkle/crease paper and card. Goes off in about 30 minutes but takes longer to set. Best to avoid contact with skin as it can irritate.
Epoxy resin	Ceramic, wood, metal	Two-part glue most often in tubes. Trade name 'Araldite' frequently found in schools. Mainly used with resistant materials to join different materials. Very strong when mixed in proportion. A catalyst is used to harden the resin. Wear eye protection when using this glue.
Spray glue	Paper, card, fabric, felt	Comes in an aerosol can and is to be applied sparingly. Use in a ventilated area as it is toxic. Some spray glues allow mounted work to be removed and re-stuck. Very quick and effective way of mounting photographs and drawings.
Hot glue	Paper, card, wood, some polymers and stone	Dispensed through a gun. Can be awkward to control and drips hot glue or 'stringy' pieces created. Sets clear and very effective for gluing welding rod into a piece of wood on a model garden or similar, but you need to rough the surface of the materials for a better bond. Use sparingly for best effect.
Tensol cement	Most polymers	Available in a variety of chemical mixes. Usually clear and a very thin liquid. Ideal for acrylic as joints are tight and the glue does not show. Toxic: the fumes can cause nausea and headaches. Must keep the lid on when not in use as it will evaporate. Can be applied with a small thin brush or through a syringe or pipette. Wear eye protection when working with this cement.
Masking tape/ sellotape	Most materials but not permanent or strong	Masking tape comes in a roll and can be used to join or cover. Good for holding cover in place when spraying a limited area. Sellotape is clear sticky-backed roll. Fixes readily to card and paper but is not easily removed without damage. Double-sided tape is useful when modelling as it can stick together two surfaces without the joint showing (even on wood), avoiding any setting time.
Super glue, Cyanoacrylate	Mainly resistant materials	Comes in a small tube or bottle and is usually clear. Will stick almost anything including skin. **Extreme care** must be exercised when used. Very strong and invisible if applied with care.

△ **Table 2.1** Different adhesives and their uses

Cont.

Glue	Works on	Description and use
Glue stick	Paper, card and some polymers (sticks paper to wood but is not too strong)	Comes in a container like a lipstick tube with a twist action to allow the white glue to be dispensed. Solvent free and washable, thus safe to use, and relatively cheap to buy. Clean, accurate and easily applied. Gives you a little adjustment time when positioning. Can be stored and used at a later date as cap seals the tube, although it does harden over time.

△ **Table 2.1** Different adhesives and their uses

Key terms

Adhesive – a substance which bonds materials together.

Solvent – a chemical which dissolves the surface of a material.

2.3 Cutting tools for graphics and modelling

A wide range of tools can be used by hand with a great deal of success, but care must be taken as many of them are very sharp. Use the knives in conjunction with a safety rule. Remember always to keep your fingers out of the way and to use a cutting mat for best results.

△ **Figure 2.5** Guillotine, safety rule, craft knife and mat

Different tools

Rotary cutter

The rotary cutter is best used freehand. Have a practice on some scrap before trying this on your project. It is not always easy to use, and some polymers require more pressure.

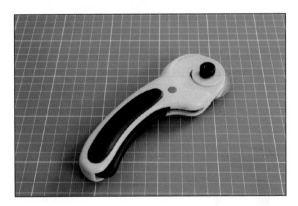

△ **Figure 2.6** A rotary cutter

Compass cutter

The compass cutter is most effectively used on paper or light card. Again, practise this before you use it on your project. Sometimes it is easier to move the paper rather than the cutter.

◁ **Figure 2.7**
A compass cutter

△ **Figure 2.9** A cutting forme

Fret saw

The fret saw can be used very effectively on thicker card and on many polymers. A jeweller's piercing saw is also useful for this type of cutting. You can use a variety of blades, which will help to get a finer finish. Be careful, though, as the blades snap quite easily.

Usually the majority of the shape is cut out and is then removed by hand. You can see in Figure 2.10 how the parts are still joined to the original large piece of material, and the operator is separating the work. This is so that the operator can remove the sheet material from the dangerous blades without being cut.

◁ **Figure 2.8** A fret saw

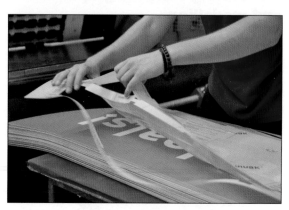

△ **Figure 2.10** An operator separates the shape from the sheet

Forme

In industry a forme is used when repeatedly cutting out a shape. This is a series of blades, as sharp as razor blades, set up on edge in the required outline. They are fixed to a piece of wood and have foam either side of the cutting edge. When the card or paper is pressed against the blade edges, the required shape is cut out. A photograph of part of a forme is shown in Figure 2.9.

Key points
- ○ Using the equipment requires a high standard of health and safety practice.
- ○ Do not take any risks that might endanger your health.
- ○ Ensure that your working environment is clean and tidy, and that you are safe.

2.4 Using components

There is a whole range available of potentially bought-in components. When modelling it is important to realise that you can make good use of some of these, even when they are not usually used for that purpose. For example, a paper fastener can be glued to a model and look very much like a knob to press for on and off.

Table 2.2 lists some of these components.

> **Activity**
> Using a rectangular piece of foam or other suitable modelling material, shape it and add components to make it look like a USB. Try to make it as lifelike as possible.

2.5 Linking graphic materials with other components

Modelling for GCSE graphics sometimes requires the use of other materials not necessarily associated with or listed as graphic materials in the specification set out by the AQA and other examination authorities.

Resistant materials such as thin beech laminates or soft iron binding wire can be very useful for creating a structure or framework for the product model. Materials can frequently be used in an alternative way rather than their initial use. When covered in a coloured felt, a glass jar or a polystyrene container can act as a container for cards or counters which form part of a game.

Some product models will not resolve enough of the form to sort out the detail. A small working model with gears, axles, motors and wheels may be needed. You are advised to buy these sorts of components, or liberate from other uses! They are time-consuming to make, and you are unlikely to create them with the level of accuracy needed in the time allowed for the coursework.

> **Exam tip**
> Students must be careful not to become too involved in the working of any mechanism, as it may not count toward the final mark, no matter how successful the resolution. For example, when some students chose to design and make a model for a bus shelter, one made lighting with LEDs. It helped with the overall impression of the model, but did not earn many extra marks and took a substantial amount of time to create.

> **Summary**
> Using graphics equipment is an essential element of the course and will be examined.
> o Using most pieces of equipment effectively requires skills which need to be learned and have to be practised.

Action	Component
fasten	paper clip, paper fastener, sticky label, staple, treasury tag
seal	encapsulation with a polymer, envelope edge, Velcro
hang	mapping pin, drawing pin, blu tak, bulldog clip
join	glue, sellotape, dry transfer, Post-it
bind	PVC slide binder, spiral made from polymer or metal, glue and press
index	clip file, dividers

△ **Table 2.2** Components to be used for modelling

chapter 3
Designers

Introduction

Looking at the work and the role of designers will help you to develop a better understanding of their work and how they influence our choices.

In today's society we control our environment and our existence more than at any stage in our history. Designers influence every aspect of our lives. Although not all design benefits us, the best design is not only functional but also aesthetically pleasing and makes our life easier.

The influence of designers is significant in social, political and economic terms. Since the early 1900s, the nature of graphic design has changed radically. The printed word has been supplemented with drawings, photographs and moving images. Before television and mass communication existed on the scale which we know today, typography was critical to the perception of the word. Two graphic designers, Edward Johnstone and Stanley Morison, influenced everyday lives with their new typefaces for the London Underground and *The Times* newspaper respectively. Propaganda and the distribution of literature for political gain became a well-trodden path. This was particularly the case before and during the Second World War. After the war, graphic artists Tom Eckersley and Reginald Mount were employed by the British Government to create influential and widely used poster designs.

Activities

Look at the posters created during the 1930s and 1940s. Select two or three posters and use them as the basis for the work. Take a theme such as 'Careless Talk' or the advertisements of the Shell company, and answer the following three questions:

1. What is the role of the image in the poster?
2. How is the designer trying to influence the response and perception of the public?
3. Why did the popularity of the poster decline?

The development of the work of the graphic designer does not happen in isolation. Changes in society, technology, new processes and materials also play a major part in the rapidly changing formats.

Today, with the advent of electronic technology, designers have become more in control of the production of their work and the processes; consequently they are even more influential in the process. Packages that were designed for foodstuffs in the 1960s are seldom used today. This is largely because the consumer has become more demanding and the manufacturer is still required to make a profit. Making the product more attractive, meeting current legislation, promoting the sale and managing the distribution have all become integral parts of the graphic designer's responsibility.

Although not as well known as product designers, some graphic designers have influenced all our lives, perhaps without our knowledge.

Below is information on a selection of graphic designers as listed by the AQA specification.

3.1 Harry Beck

Henry Charles Beck (1902–74) designed the first outline London Underground map in 1931. It was trialled in 1932 and came into commission in 1933. The map was based on a geographical layout in a linear form with no allowance for the relative distances between stations. Most importantly, it was clear, easy to use and supplied only necessary information such as the relative positions of stations and where passengers could change from one line to another. The use of colours was vital for this clarity.

◁ **Figure 3.1**
Harry Beck

Beck started the work out of his own interest, and developed it sometimes with and sometimes without the agreement of London Underground. Not all of his ideas and suggested changes were accepted or implemented. Another designer, Harold Hutchinson, introduced the Victoria line to the map, and designer Paul Garbutt introduced the lozenge-shaped Circle line.

Harry Beck also produced schematic maps for the rail network in London. He later taught typography and colour design at the London School of Printing and Kindred Trades.

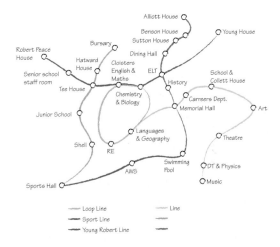

△ **Figure 3.2** A map of a school site

3.2 Alberto Alessi

Alberto Alessi (1946–) was born in Italy, the son of an industrial designer. The family company, Alessi, was founded in 1921 to create metal products for eating and drinking. Alessi joined the family business in 1970 after taking a degree in law. The business has frequently relied upon freelance designers for many of its products.

One of the business's strengths has been their willingness to use modern materials and give existing products an amusing twist; designing with a sense of fun yet retaining the functional element of the product. Figure 3.4 shows Alessi products with lively colours and simple forms.

Key term

Function – the action for which a person or thing is particularly fitted or employed.

△ **Figure 3.3** Alberto Alessi

△ **Figure 3.4** Alessi designs

Activity

Design a simple counter that could be used on a Monopoly board. It does not have to be one of the traditional pieces like the iron or car, but can be of your choice.

o The piece is to be in the style of the Alessi work.
o It should be made from brightly coloured material.
o It can be fun rather than serious.
o It must be capable of being handled, but not too clumsily.
o It must be able to be packed away for use at another time.
o It must be cheap to make.

Exam tip

The Alessi designs are very distinctive. You could be asked to compare these with the work of another designer.

3.3 **Jock Kinneir and Margaret Calvert**

Together, Richard 'Jock' Kinneir (1917–74) and Margaret Calvert (1936–) designed the road and motorway signage system.

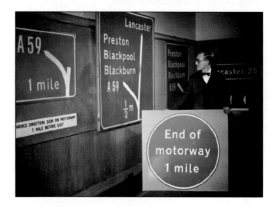

△ **Figure 3.5** Jock Kinneir

Jock Kinneir studied engraving at the Chelsea School of Art and started work as an exhibition designer for the Central Office of Information. He designed the signage system for Gatwick airport and lectured at the Chelsea School of Art. It was here that he met Margaret Calvert, a student at the time. She began to work with him, initially in assistance, and as a full business partner in 1964.

△ **Figure 3.7** Kinneir and Calvert created the road signage system

◁ **Figure 3.6**
Margaret Calvert

In 1957, when independent travel by car was becoming available for many people, the Government commissioned a signage system for the intended motorways. Until that time, road signage was haphazard and unsuitable for travel at speed. Kinneir and Calvert created a system which uniformly coordinated lettering, colour, shape and symbol; all for use on the new motorways. They designed and used a combination of upper- and lower-case letters, now known as the 'transport' typeface. It was easy to read and set out in a manner that enabled consistency across the range. Each letter was placed as if on a tile and spaced accordingly. They created a code or set of rules which were used as guidelines for the designs.

This solution was later used as the basis for all other road signage. Using the existing conventions of circles to command, triangles to warn, and rectangles to inform, they created a range of signage to help the motorist. Colours played an important role, just as they had in

the motorway signage. The white lettering was retained but the blue background gave way to a green background, and the numbers of the roads were in yellow. However, this was only used for the major roads. The minor roads were written in black on a white background.

△ **Figure 3.8** A road sign showing a ring road

Key terms

Typography – the art and technique of printing with movable type.

Typeface – a set of one or more fonts, in one or more sizes, designed with stylistic unity each comprising a coordinated set of characters.

◁ **Figure** 3.9 A road sign indicating no cars or motorbikes

On 1 January 1965, the signage became law. When the work was digitised by the Department of Transport, much of the original artwork and layout instructions were used, and are still in use today.

Later in their partnership, Kinneir and Calvert worked on projects for British Rail and the Tyne and Weir Metro signage projects.

Activity

Design a typeface for the initial letters of your first name and your surname.

○ Use a combination of vertical, horizontal and lines at 45 degrees.
○ The thickness of the line can vary.
○ Try to develop a common theme to the initials.
○ Use only black typeface.
○ Do not include any curves in the ideas.

Key point

It is essential that the characters used stay constant.

3.4 **Wally Olins**

From a Jewish immigrant family, Wally Olins (1930–) studied at Oxford and worked initially in advertising. In 1965 he founded a partnership with Michael Wolff, the Wolff Olins consultancy. Later he became one of the foremost image marketing gurus, and arguably the world's leading branding expert. Olins left the consultancy in 2001 to found the Saffron Brand Consultants with Jacob Benbunan. He was awarded the CBE in 1999.

△ **Figure 3.10** Wally Olins

Part of his work in the creation of identity, brand and communication with the people he worked with was to create corporate images. Many of these are familiar to us all, as the clients were prestigious firms such as 3i, Repsol, Renault, Volkswagen and Gulf Petroleum (Q8). Kuwait Petroleum, a subsidiary of Gulf Petroleum, changed its name to Q8 in 1986 based on the English pronunciation of Kuwait. The twin sails of the logo refer to the traditional Kuwaiti trading ship, and the bright colours enable the signage to stand out more boldly.

△ **Figure 3.11** Olins's Q8 logo

Activity

Create a logo or corporate identity for a local gym. Be sure it complies with the following requirements:

o The logo will be on all of the stationery used by the gym.
o It will be part of the advertising material.
o A maximum of three colours should be used.
o The logo can include an image that suggests activity and energy.
o It is important that the name of the gym is created and included.
o Suggest that attendance at the gym is part of a healthy lifestyle.

Exam tip

If you are designing a logo ensure that your final idea is obviously related to the information given. It is too easy to move your idea away from the information given if you are not careful.

3.5 Robert Sabuda

Born in 1965, Robert Sabuda is a creator of children's books with superb pop-ups. He attended college at the Pratt Institute in New York. See the website (www. robertsabuda. com) for many examples of his work. His work is an ideal stimulus for GCSE projects.

△ **Figure 3.12** A page from a pop-up book

◁ **Figure 3.13**
Robert Sabuda

Sabuda became interested in 3D paper engineering as a result of a visit to the dentist where he encountered a pop-up book for the first time. After leaving college he carried out some work as a package designer and worked independently on some children's books. He illustrated his first children's book series, Bulky Board Books, in 1987.

Interestingly, Sabuda puts the text of the book on a fold to the side of the page, and this too has a separate element which pops up. He is constantly trying to bring an element of surprise and intrigue to the page, regardless of the age of the reader. Beware too, as he says that it is harder to make it pop flat than it is to make it pop up.

The important aspect of the book is the story and not the mechanism. As Sabuda says, 'For the most part, the reader is oblivious to the "technical" aspects of a mechanical book … and that's the way it should be. They shouldn't be focusing on the "how" of the book, they should be enjoying the book for the sake of the experience.'

Other paper engineers have also released their own books, copies of which are readily available. Paul Johnson, David A. Carter and James Diaz have some excellent work which enables step-by-step progress, to be easily understood by students.

Exam tip

Pop-ups have seldom been used in the exam but can be easily illustrated if you practise drawing them. They make very effective and energetic solutions, which the average student tends not to use.

Key points

○ Look particularly at the work of the six designers, but not exclusively.
○ Successful designs have clarity and a simplicity about them.

Exam practice questions

1. Using four different Alessi designs, create a table showing clearly the similarities and differences of the products.

2. Using the typeface you created when completing the work on Kinneir and Calvert, apply this to packaging for a toothpaste container. Your product should be aimed at children between the ages of three and seven. When you have finished, evaluate how effective your solution is for this purpose.

3. Look carefully at the London Olympics logo. What elements of this design could be altered to improve the overall impression?

4. Using an existing sign system (for example, for your school or college) make some changes that improve on the existing system and cater for the multicultural nature of our society.

Summary

Looking at designers' work will help you to get a better understanding of how to approach the exam. You need to consider a range of designers who have been producing their ideas in differing cultures and times. In the exam you will be asked to design for a specific purpose or application, so always try to create your ideas within a brief or to meet a specification. If the project you are undertaking doesn't have a brief or specification then outline one for yourself.

It is more important to understand and be able to discuss the influence and effects of the designers on society, rather than learn their dates of birth and where they worked. The designer's work is important in that it tells us about them but it also helps us to understand it as a part of the world they live(d) in. The designers listed for the exam are important, but they are not an exhaustive list. When researching for this section you will come across other designers whose work you like and who are worth spending a bit of time on. Try to recognise the style and the influences on the work. Look carefully at the materials and techniques being used. Determine what it is you like about the work and why.

Learning objectives

By the end of this chapter you should have developed a knowledge and understanding of:

o how to communicate a concept to a potential client, manufacturer or purchaser
o the functions of mock-ups, models and prototypes and the importance they can play in the design process
o how 'target marketing' and 'gap in the market' identification are used to promote a product
o how to produce quality 2D and 3D sketches
o how to use crating techniques, grids and underlays to produce drawings
o key words in presenting a design
o sketching textures
o how colour can help in the presentation of a design
o contrast, complementary, hue and tone
o the language of colour
o colour fusion and separation and their commercial application
o the importance of high-quality presentation
o aspects of typography and lettering anatomy
o perspective (one point or two point) and isometric drawings
o how to use third-angle orthographic projection to British Standard Conventions (BS8888, 2006)
o how to demonstrate use of self-assembly, sectional and exploded drawings
o how to use and understand scale drawings
o how to interpret room, site plans and maps
o how a 2D shape can be made into a 3D form
o how a development can be fastened or assembled
o how the processes and equipment change when many outcomes are required
o representing data in graphical form; i. e. 2D and 3D bar and pie charts, line graphs and pictographs
o the language of labels and signage and the function and uses of corporate identity
o how to produce ideograms, pictograms and symbols; flowcharts with feedback loops; sequential illustrations; schematic maps.

Introduction

Graphic designers must be able to communicate a concept to a potential client or manufacturer and show the function of mock-ups, models and prototypes in the design process. This chapter examines a range of techniques and processes used by graphic designers as part of the design process, including sketching; enhancement techniques; presentation methods; pictorial, working and information drawings; and surface development. To promote a product, you must also be able to identify how target marketing and gaps in the market are used.

4.1 The designer's role

Graphic designers communicate their ideas in a range of media for the users to understand the ideas and concepts. It is important that clients clearly understand the ideas and concepts.

Communication can be through a meeting to explain concepts and ideas verbally, or through drawings that have notes attached and annotations to explain the details. Another method of presenting design ideas is through the use of mock-ups, models and prototypes. These can be produced to ensure that the designs are fully understood and can be constructed in a material and to a scale that best suit the client's demands.

The graphic designer must communicate a concept in a way that is understood by the potential client, manufacturer or purchaser.

△ **Figure 4.1** Architectural model

Communicating a concept

When the graphic designer starts the design process for the client, manufacturer or purchaser, they will produce lots of ideas that need to be refined. Some ideas will be discarded, while others will be developed. Some designers choose to decide which to consider by producing mock-ups of some of the ideas.

When constructing a mock-up, the objective is to produce it quickly, using materials such as card, paper, foam board, double-sided tape and useful scraps.

Immediately the designer can then receive some user feedback and make reference against the user design specification, to see if the model meets with the designer's original ideas for the product.

At this stage the designer may also want to do a survey of the target market with the mock-up or prototypes, to gain a more accurate understanding of how the product will perform for the client, manufacturer or purchaser. The designer will now select their final ideas, which will be continually refined to meet the specification.

Development of ideas

For communication with the client, Computer-Aided Design (CAD) software can be used, to produce a number of images with different views and presentation options. (See Chapter 8 for further information on CAD.) Changes can quickly and easily be made on screen, which shows computer-generated models of a graphical product. The designer should consult with the client to ensure that drawings can be exchanged in a form that can be read by both computer systems (for example, as a JPEG).

There are benefits to using a CAD package to communicate with the client, manufacturer or purchaser:

1. It is easy to change aspects of the design without having to change the entire thing.

2. It is possible to produce a whole range of colours, views, and styles.

3. Designers can receive feedback and then have a conversation about any changes required by the users.

4. It can help to ensure that you are making a product that meets the need.

Modelling ideas

Modelling materials used by the designer will depend on the type of project or the part of the project being modelled. Models can be in the form of a 2D sketch. Communication at the early stages of the design process will be based on initial ideas and will lack some detail, but sketches may clear up any basic confusion. You should be able to develop your simple 2D sketch using 3D sketching and modelling.

When a 3D model is used in the early stages of the design process, it can be a very powerful tool to explain ideas. A 3D model can be viewed from all sides, and a judgement can be made on whether or not it looks as the designer and user intended.

As the designer begins to refine the concepts, a variety of different 3D models can be produced. For the designer and the client it is far more cost-effective to make mistakes with a mock-up and model rather than later on during the manufacture of the product.

Prototype ideas

Designers may be expected to produce a prototype of the design idea(s), just as manufacturers would in industry. When the designer presents the prototype to the client, details on how the finished object will be manufactured should be included, such as the materials used, the colours selected and any feedback from possible users on the product's performance.

Key term

Computer-Aided Design (CAD) – drawing on a computer, which can be viewed in 2D and 3D.

4.2 Mock-ups, models and prototypes

Mock-ups, models and prototypes should show what the final designed product will look like when manufactured. The ideas can be represented by 3D models, but can also be 2D drawings and computer renderings. Models in the real world are used to show clients, manufacturers or customers the design, because for some people it can be easier to understand a constructed concept than a drawing.

All car manufacturers produce prototypes of new vehicles. These working models are life-size and can be used for development, testing and evaluation. A vehicle prototype would also be used to test market response; if the idea was not well received in a market survey, perhaps the design would not be manufactured.

△ **Figure 4.2** Model aeroplane

Appropriate scale

A model may not always be made to actual size. As part of the design process, manufacturers will make a model, mock-up or prototype to the appropriate scale in order to understand the concept. It would be impossible for a designer to show the client a full-size model of an office development, therefore the designer must make a scale model appropriate for the design.

Table 4.1 shows typical examples of scale.

Activity

Measure a room in your house, and then draw it on an A4 piece of paper (in plan view) to some form of scale. Include some of the tables and chairs in the room. Show clearly the scale used.

Term	Description
Jewellery	twice full size
Phone	Full size
Point of sale	half size
Club interior	1 to 100
Stadium	1 to 500
Housing estate	1 to 1,000

△ **Table 4.1** Typical examples of scale

Why use models and mock-ups?

The designer should be able to develop a simple 2D sketch using 3D sketching and modelling. The material used will depend on the type of project or the part of the project being modelled. A 2D sketch model will be based on initial ideas and will lack some detail, but it may clear up some misunderstanding with the client.

Designers find that it is often helpful to make 3D models in the early stages of the design process, because a visual 3D product can be a good representation of an idea or concept. The advantage of a 3D model is that it can be viewed from all sides, and you can judge whether or not it looks as you intended. Discussion with the client at this early stage can stimulate a range of new ideas, such as the use of different materials. It is far more cost-effective to make mistakes with a paper or card model early on than in the final product.

Key terms

Mock-up – a model, often full-size, of a design to allow for evaluation; a working model of a product built for study, testing or display.

Model – a smaller sometimes scaled-down version of the design. Graphic representation of a product.

Prototype – working model of a design, used for testing, development and evaluation (life-size).

4.3 Target marketing to promote a product

The purpose of good business is to design, make and sell products which are a commercial success. The designer must find out who is part of the target market for the products. One simple but time-consuming way of finding out is to ask questions to people in the target market. Surveys of different markets should be based on factors such as attitudes and values, gender, age, interests, occupation, and socio-economic grouping.

Market surveys can be carried out face to face, in which a researcher approaches members of the public and asks them to fill in a questionnaire. Marketing now makes far more use of data gathered over the internet, to predict how well a product meets the need of the marketplace, and to spot opportunities to develop new products.

Information gathered from market surveys may help a producer to find out what their customers need. If the marketplace tells the survey that a different product is needed, the company may design and make a product to meet the demand, or change a product so that it is better suited to what people need. If there is not a product to meet the need of the customer, this is described as a 'gap in the market'.

△ **Figure 4.3** Identifying a target market

Exam tip

If possible, the designer will try to find a gap or niche in the market. Try to answer the examination questions with fresh examples.

Key term

Target market – the group of people to whom you are aiming your design.

Activity

Apple designed the iPod touch and the iPhone. Imagine what might be the next range of products to be produced.

4.4 Sketching

Sketching is an important technique in a designer's toolkit. Sketching:

○ allows you to develop your ideas
○ allows others to understand your ideas
○ shows a skill that adds value to your work.

Designers tend to sketch in several styles. The styles are clear, efficient and often follow guidelines and rules.

Sketching often follows a framework, which means that anyone can sketch if they follow the rules. It can be taught and it can be learned. Practice helps; the more you practise, the quicker and more accurate you become.

Producing and annotating 2D and 3D sketches

Ideas can be illustrated using two-dimensional (**2D**) or three-dimensional (**3D**) drawings. Drawings in 2D look flat; they show only two dimensions of your work, usually width and height. If you want to show the depth of your design, you can illustrate this in a 3D drawing.

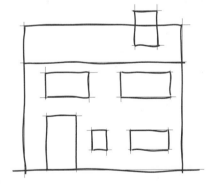

△ **Figure 4.4** A 2D drawing of a house; note that this view does not show depth

Whatever style or styles of drawings you use on your page it is important to add notes – **annotation.** Notes help you develop your work, and they allow a **third party** to understand your reasoning. Notes mention the changes you will make, materials and manufacturing processes you might use, or can even be placed just to help you remember your train of thought.

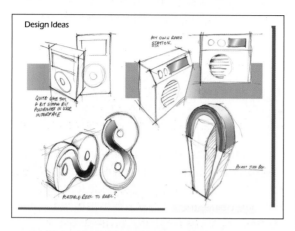

△ **Figure 4.5** An annotated sketch

Two-dimensional drawing

Two-dimensional drawing could be a print, a graphic, or image of a 3D item shown in a style called **orthographic drawing.** An orthographic drawing is a very formal style of drawing used by architects, engineers and designers all over the world. It can be used like an international language; with orthographic drawing, designers can communicate with people from different countries and cultures. However, like a language, it has structure and rules. It is important to follow these rules so that your ideas are understood and make sense.

In orthographic drawing, different views are used to represent a single object. When these are placed in the right order, a drawing can be read.

Key term

Orthographic drawing – formal style of drawing used worldwide.

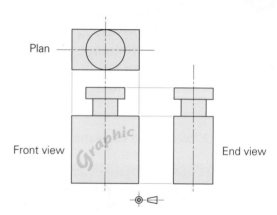

△ **Figure 4.6** Orthographic drawing is in 2D with a specific layout, showing height, depth and length

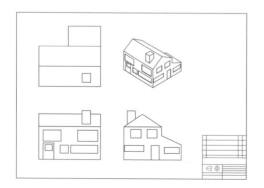

△ **Figure 4.7** Orthographic drawing in third and first angle

Three-dimensional drawing

Many types of 3D drawings are used by designers. These fall into three categories:

1. obliques
2. axiometrics
3. perspectives.

Some are more suited to illustrating different outcomes than others. It is your choice which to use; there is no right or wrong style to use. However, the style which you choose should have more clarity or more impact than other styles.

Oblique

Oblique views have one face of the item square on. Angled away from this is drawn a view to show depth. Parallel angled lines are used when the height and depth are constant.

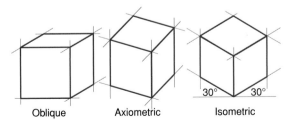

△ **Figure 4.8** Oblique, axiometric and isometric drawing

Axiometric

Axiometric drawings use parallel lines to represent height in two different views. The angle of these lines from the horizontal may vary. If both are 30 degrees, the style is **isometric**. This is the most commonly used style.

If the angles used are the same but not 30 degrees, the style is called **diametric**. If different angles are used, it is a **trimetric** drawing.

△ **Figure 4.9** Diametric and triametric drawing

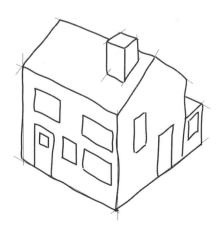

△ **Figure 4.10** A 3D drawing of a house. Depth can be seen in this style of view

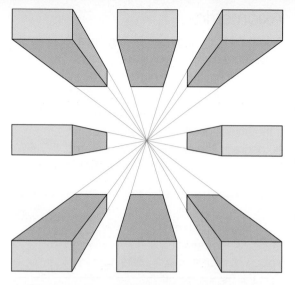

△ **Figure 4.11** A 3D single-point perspective

Perspective

Perspective views can give the most photorealistic outcome. The lines drawn to illustrate depth are not parallel, but converge onto a point. If the lines converge onto one point, the style is **single-point perspective**. If two points are used, the style is called **two-point perspective**; three points can be used to give a **three-point perspective** drawing.

○ Single-point perspective is often used by interior designers to illustrate inside rooms.
○ Two-point perspectives give a product designer a way of illustrating small devices.
○ Three-point perspectives allow architects to give a feeling of great height to a presentation of a building.

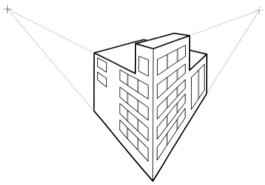

△ **Figure 4.12** A 3D two-point perspective

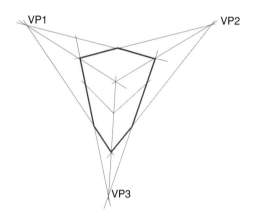

△ **Figure 4.13** A 3D three-point perspective

 Activity
Draw a high street in two-point perspective. Take particular care with signs that stick out, and the spacing between regularly spaced objects.

Crating

It is useful to practise drawing simple shapes, such as cubes, pyramids, cylinders, rectangles. These can be placed together like building blocks to form more complex shapes. If the base form is accurate and in proportion, the complex form will also be correct.

Imagine you have been given a gift in a tight-fitting box. The shape of the gift box gives the proportion of the product that is inside. If the box can be drawn accurately, this is a good starting point for the framework.

Inside the crate the outline of the shape of the product can be sketched. The outline of the shape can be made to look as if it was made out of wire. Seeing through the product helps you visualise the whole form. Drawing an occasional line following the shape of the surface also helps you to see how the shape looks (blue pencil is often used by professional designers).

> **Activity**
> Using a crate, sketch a product that you can see in your classroom; for example, a pencil sharpener. Be critical of your work; try to keep the form in proportion.

△ **Figure 4.15** Blue pencil lines can be used to draw the crate. The form can be further enhanced by using the blue pencil to follow the shape of the object

Grids and overlays

Sketching can be completed in many forms. Freehand drawings are often used at the early part of the design process. These sketches can be done by eye but still follow the rules of formal illustration. This enhances the creative experience, as more detail is added so the accuracy improves. At a later stage, rulers and

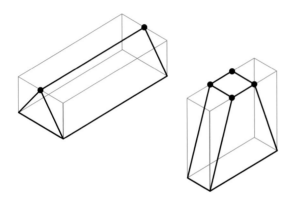

△ **Figure 4.14** Sketching an accurate crate will keep your drawing in proportion

△ **Figure 4.16** A grid can be used to scale a drawing: copy each square in the grid exactly to magnify the drawing

straight edges can be used to ensure that the idea is dimensionally sound.

Grids and **overlays** can be used to give freehand sketches accuracy in proportion and keep the drawing visually correct. This is not cheating! A professional trick saves time and can give better results.

Grids

Grids can take several forms. They can be used to ensure that lines sketched over the top of them are parallel, or that spacings look right. Grids can also be used to scale a drawing up or down, or be used to distort the original shape.

Activity
Draw a square grid over a picture. On a new piece of paper, redraw this square grid twice the size. Carefully note where the picture crosses the original grid. Copy these points onto the large grid, then complete the picture.

Leaving an extension of a grid on the drawing can help with the presentation of the end result.

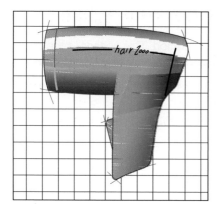

△ **Figure 4.17** A background grid can help the illustration visually and give a technical appearance

Grids are useful when contructing lettering. Most capital letters can be constructed in a 5 x 3 grid. The exception is M and W; these are wider letters and need a 5 x 5 grid.

Activity
Choose five letters of the alphabet not shown in the illustration. Create these in a grid.

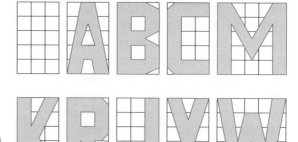

△ **Figure 4.18** Capital letters can be created in a 3 x 5 grid

Overlays

Overlays are used to help the development of an idea. A piece of semi-transparent paper is laid over an existing drawing or shape. This is then used as a guide to trace through. The framework that is seen through the paper can be changed and adapted. Quick copies can be made to show different colourways, or the bulk of the shape is copied and quick changes are made.

Speed is important to a designer. Sketching should be quick and accurate, but should not slow down the thought process of an emerging design. Overlaying allows speed to be supported by accuracy.

Basic shapes drawn on a computer program can be printed off and used as an overlay. Shapes such as cylinders that are considered difficult can be accurately reproduced in a freehand format after tracing them through from a CAD drawing. These CAD drawings need not be complex. The block shapes are used as a drawing template, allowing proportion, form and perspective to be controlled.

△ **Figure 4.19** A simple CAD drawing can be used as an underlay to sketch over; this helps to keep ellipses accurate

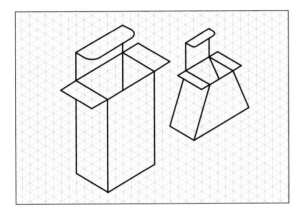

△ **Figure 4.20** Isometric grids are commonly used as a guide to illustrations

Key terms

Annotation – adding notes to a design.

Oblique – views that have one face of the item square on.

Axiometric – using parallel lines to represent height in two different views.

Perspectives – lines drawn to illustrate depth; they converge on a point.

Crating – used to draw simple shapes, which are put together to form more complex shapes.

4.5 Enhancement

A simple test to evaluate whether or not a design is successful is to see how well it functions. However, it is also important for the design to be visually exciting and appealing. Consider the iPod: the look and feel are important selling points, as well as how it performs musically.

In design, the visual quality **(aesthetic)** mostly deals with shape, proportion, pattern, texture and colour. These work together to give the product its look and style. Before the product is made, it is important that the designer offers a representation of the aesthetic in their sketching and block models.

Proportion and texture

Proportion

Proportion is the balance or ratio of the height to the width of a shape. Different proportions will make a shape look elegant, dumpy, squat, thin, etc. By adding texture and pattern, the proportion of a shape can be disguised to make it feel different.

△ **Figure 4.21** Proportion is important to the aesthetic of a product. These candles are made the same way but look very different because of their proportion

Texture

Texture is the reflection, or lack of reflection, of light off a surface. Shiny, rough or smooth all describe the texture of an object. These textures can be represented on drawings to show the viewer how the shape would feel.

Textures can be random or regular. In natural products such as wood, the texture can be considered random. Regular textures are usually man-made, such as grooves down the side of a cap. In instances like this, the texture is functional; it offers grip to the user. Random-made textures are often used to give a non-slip surface; they also help to hide scratches and wear on a product.

Activity
Colour the shapes to show light and shade.

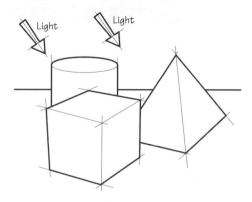

△ **Figure 4.22** Use the shapes shown and try to illustrate how they can be coloured to show light and shade. Imagine that the light is shining from the top left of the page

Tricks or techniques can be used to give different impressions of your drawings. Texture makes a drawing more interesting. It can also clearly represent what material the product will be made from.

Activity
Add the textures shown in Figure 4.23 to the shading blocks above.

△ **Figure 4.23** Textures can be added with the use of line and colour

Colour

Colour is another crucial factor in how a product looks or feels. Colour has a language; the colours you choose can make a product feel fun, classical or safe, for example. Think about medical products and the clean, efficient colours that are used on the labelling or packaging.

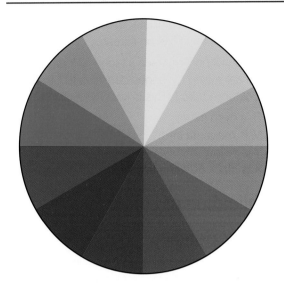

△ **Figure 4.24** The colour wheel helps to balance colours on a design

Language of colour

Colour is reflected white light that we see from objects, posters and print. The surface absorbs some of the spectrum, and we see what is bounced back. Colour has its own vocabulary. Below are some key words that help describe colour and its range.

Primary colours are the three base shades that when mixed can make all other colours. These are red, yellow and blue.

If two primary colours are mixed, **secondary** colours are formed; for example:

o orange = red and yellow
o violet = red and blue
o green = yellow and blue.

When an additional primary colour is added to a secondary colour, a **tertiary** colour is formed. The process can be repeated many times to form a range of different colours or **hues**. The hues can be made lighter by adding white, or darker by mixing in black. The darker version of the colour is called a **shade**; the lighter version is a **tint**.

To help guide us through the use of colour, colours are often represented in a colour wheel; see Figure 4.24. In its basic form the wheel is in six segments. Each primary colour is separated by the secondary colour formed when mixing the primaries either side of it. The wheel is useful when choosing colours that will be used together.

Colours opposite each other on the colour wheel **contrast** each other, and are called **complementary** colours. These colours stand out from each other and are useful when highlighting text or creating something that will stand out.

Colours next to (or close to) each other on the colour wheel are called **harmonious**. These blend well together, giving a subtle, comfortable feel.

o Reds, yellows and oranges are described as **warm colours**, like fire. These can be used to give a welcoming or comforting effect to a product or a poster.
o Blues are **cool colours**, like ice. These tend to be used when a product is efficient or clinical.
o Black and white are not strictly colours. However, when used on a product they can have a striking effect.
o **Neutral colours** are greys, beiges, creams and soft whites. These are useful on large surfaces when the effect should not be overpowering.
o **Natural colours** such as browns, greens and yellows are thought to be restful.

 Activity
Design a sign for a fish and chip shop. Change the design so that it uses:
1. all warm colours
2. all cool colours
3. contrasting colours.
Decide which looks the most effective.

Colour and emotion

Emotions and feelings are linked with colour. Colour theorists have developed a range of responses around different colours:

o Blue – cool loyal colour, secure, male-orientated, sea, sky, peace, calm
o Yellow – brightness, sunlight, happy, cowardice, caution
o Red – danger, aggression, heat, passion
o Brown – earth, soil, rustic, natural
o Green – jealousy, inexperience, health, envy, greed, money
o Purple – sophisticated, royal
o Orange – excitement, energy, warmth, fire
o Pink – feminine, healthy, soft, childlike
o White – simple, elegant, pure, clean
o Grey – neutral (can be warm or cool), businesslike
o Black – classy, evil, modern, mourning, dramatic.

Referencing and registering colours

Millions of colours are used in industry. It is not enough to say that you want to use a red: a precise red must be specified. Companies spend thousands of pounds in generating a logo. This will be used and manufactured all over the word. The company and designers need to ensure that the colour is the same.

Several colour referencing systems are used as a standard so that printers and manufacturers use and select the correct colour. Pantone is one such recognised standard. A code is used to describe the precise colour. It is possible to get a free downloadable application for the iPhone that will recognise any colour and convert it to a printing code.

Another way of registering colours is to specify the amount of red, yellow, and blue in the colour. A code is then applied to give the tint or shade. This can be seen on programs such as Adobe Photoshop. The code typed in anywhere in the world will recognised. Free downloads are also available for your computer that will recognise the colour of any pixel on screen.

Commercial printing uses a blend of four colours. These are mixed in various densities to produce the colour required. This is known as CMYK:

o C is cyan (blue)
o M is magenta (red)
o Y is yellow
o K is black (K is the last letter of black).

Application of colour

Colour pencils

Colour can be applied to your work in a variety of media. One of the quickest, easiest and most underrated medium is colour pencil. Colour pencils are a versatile form of applying texture, colour and depth to your sketches.

Several styles and techniques can be used with colour pencil. They can represent material or surface detail, and be used to highlight important aspects of your designs.

Tone

Tone is useful when applying colour, to give depth to the work. Tone can vary from very dark to white. A graduated use of tone will give a curved effect if the shading is applied along the axis of the curve.

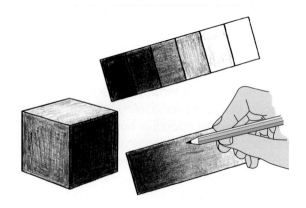

△ **Figure 4.25** Pencil tone gives the feeling of tone and depth to a drawing

Light, medium and dark tones can be used to illustrate the three faces of a product. See Figure 4.25. Notice that the direction of the shading is important. The change in the pencil line enhances the illustration of faces on different planes. This three-tone technique benefits from the pencil strokes being parallel and crossing the whole of the face. If short parallel lines are used, they can give an impression of the surface being disrupted and uneven where they meet.

Parallel shading

Parallel shading lifts the idea from the page and gives an illusion of the idea floating off the page. Placing a different view behind the given object gives an even greater effect.

Using two different colours, orange and brown, enables wood grain to be illustrated.

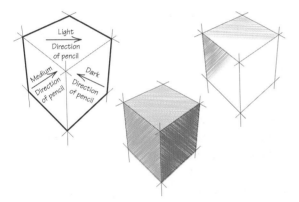

△ **Figure 4.26** Parallel shading gives your design pages depth

See Figure 4.26: notice how the direction of the line changes. This helps to create a 3D optical illusion of the shape's faces being at different angles. The parallel pencil lines are drawn as one line all across the face. Start the medium and dark sides with the same weight of line as the light. Then build up the layers, pressing harder each time.

Thickness and weight of the outside line help give the drawings excitement and life.

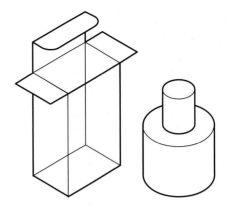

△ **Figure 4.27** The weight of lines can add interest and clarity to a drawing

Glass is usually blue or green in hue. By placing light parallel stokes on a white surface, the illusion of glass is observed. Other textures can also be added.

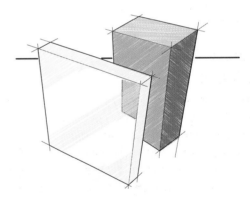

△ **Figure 4.28** Colour pencils helping to illustrate a glass surface. Use broken patches of parallel lines across the surface

Pens

A variety of pens can be used to apply colour. Unlike a pencil, the pressure of application will not affect the density of colour. However, repeating the pen over the pattern can change the tone of the ink. With a marker, the third stoke usually achieves colour saturation.

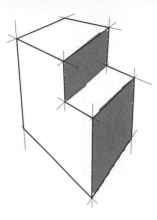

△ **Figure 4.29** Markers give a flat colour to an illustration

Pens can achieve texture, depending upon the style in which the pen is applied. Hatching and cross-hatching can give an impression of surface texture as well as applying tone and shadow to an image.

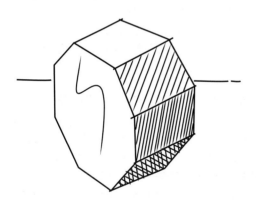

△ **Figure 4.30** Additional tone can be added by the density of the pen line

o A fine line pen can be used to add detail and highlight an aspect of a product. Pens can be used with colour pencil, with one being applied over the other.
o A white pencil, pen or wax-based crayon will allow highlights to be applied to your sketches.
o Water-soluble pencils and paints can be used to good effect on your work. One issue to address here is that the water will distort the paper when applied. This can be overcome

by using a heavy weight of paper, or by stretching the paper before application.

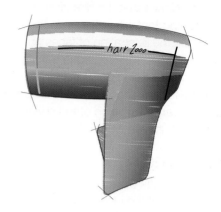

△ **Figure 4.31** White pens or white pencils can add highlights to a drawing

4.6 Presentation

The presentation of your work is very important. Your design folder should contain a range of imaginative ideas, with clear annotation referencing materials, manufacture, sustainability and reason for choice. This will move into the development section. Ideas are considered; detail and exploration of user needs are shown, with models to help support changes in the design. Your final design then needs to be clearly represented.

Presentation boards

When you fully understand and develop your design or graphic, this needs to be identified as such and illustrated. A high-quality presentation will not only benefit your GCSE project, but presentation boards are also used in industry when presenting the final idea to the client for their approval. This could cover between one and four sheets, depending on what you want to show and highlight within your ideas.

Your presentation boards could include the following:

o exploded drawings
o cut-away sections
o orthographic drawings

- sequence diagrams
- perspective drawings
- isometric drawings
- the product placed in its environment
- texture detail, material selection and manufacturing process
- a title block
- a tag line or brief description of what your product does (between three and five key points)
- photographs of models
- CAD renderings.

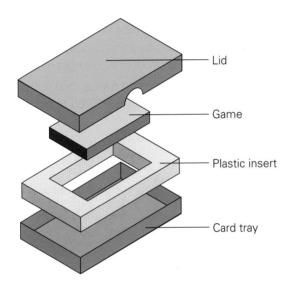

Lid

Game

Plastic insert

Card tray

△ **Figure 4.32** Simple products can be presented as an exploded drawing. This gives a clear understanding of the components and a visually exciting image

Activity

Use sequence diagrams to show how the menu system of a mobile phone or digital camera would be used.

Choice of colour

In industry, presentation boards often use a few colours only. Try to keep yours to two or three colours; think about the colour theory and harmonising or contrasting colours. If you are using a CAD package, a good technique is to choose and pixilate a picture, zoom close up, and then pick some of the colours that you can see on the screen. This often helps in selecting colours that work together.

Highlight colours from a picture or magazine page. Use three of these as a colour base for your presentation drawing

Balance and composition

The balance and composition of the board are an important key to holding the viewer's interest. Try to balance your page with colour and density of image; think about the composition and the angles of your product. Would it be more meaningful if it was illustrated from a different viewpoint?

The presentation boards need to be planned; they are almost a mini-design project themselves. Use thumbnail sketches to plot out how the boards will look. Consider which boards will hold what information. For example, you could have a technical board, a user board and a final realisation board. How will you link all three? Tie them together with the use of the same colour and borders; use the same font or logo as a theme, as seen on different pages on a website.

△ **Figure 4.33** Planning your presentation boards is important; it helps to ensure that the detail and clarity of your idea are communicated

A good presentation of your idea can be as strong an element as the idea itself.

Activity

Complete six thumbnail layouts for a product you have recently designed. Highlight which sketch shows your idea the best.

The title should be clear and precise. If you are designing a product for a child, the writing and text do not need to be childlike. As a rule of thumb, the title, border and graphic theme should not take more than a sixth of the page.

The choice of text is also very important, both the font and the actual words. Annotation can be very powerful; the presentation boards should be

able to sell your product without you being there. Check your spelling and your grammar. Use bullet points, keep the text concise.

Typography

Fonts are the style of lettering you use in your text. You have probably used several of these if you have used a computer to generate text. The use of letter styles and design is called **typography**. Graphic designers design their own fonts, but as many millions of fonts already exist, often the decision is choosing the right one. The style of font can convey different emotions, and give a feeling of elegance, fun or strength. It is important for advertisers to choose the font which will place their product in the right market.

When designing or choosing a letter or a font, key parts of that font can be identified to aid your decision.

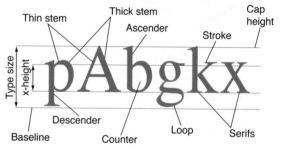

△ **Figure 4.35** The anatomy of letters: by changing parts of the letter, new styles can be generated

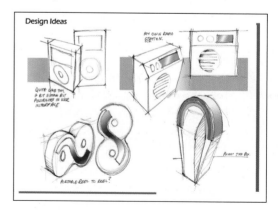

△ **Figure 4.34** In the first example, the border and titles dominate the sheet; in the second example, the titling is clear, and the product is the main focus

- o The **stem** is the vertical stroke of the letter.
- o The **serifs** are the little tails added to the end of letters.
- o The **ascender** is the part above the main body of a lower-case letter.
- o The **descender** is the part below the main body of a lower-case letter.
- o The bar or cross bar is the horizontal line of the letter.
- o The space between letters is known as **kerning**.
- o Capital letters are known as **upper** case.
- o Small letters are known as **lower** case.
- o If a letter does not have a serif, it is known as **sans serif** (French for 'without serif').
- o **Bold** text has a thicker, heavier style.
- o **Italics** are letters which slope.
- o The height of a piece of text is measured in **points**. A 72-point text will be an inch high (25.4 mm).

When choosing a font, using a lower-case word like 'hop' can help the decision, as it will show how the ascenders and descenders look. The 'h' gives an idea of the letters 'n' and 'm'; the 'p' has a round main body and can be used for second-guessing 'b' and 'q'. The 'o' is an indication of a round letter.

Activity

Print the word 'hop' in lower case in several typefaces. Note on each face the serif, the ascender and the descender.

Magazines are a great source of inspiration for the current use of fonts. They are also a good example of page layouts.

Activity

Collect pages from magazines that you find interesting. Using Post-it notes, label how the text and font sizes help to clarify the information on the page.

Activity

In your title, block change one letter by using one of the following:

- o change the font size
- o alter the colour
- o make it bold or italic
- o mirror it.

Changing one letter is often enough; too much manipulation can be confusing to the reader.

Using ICT to promote final design

Desktop publishing packages (DTP) are often used in schools to develop magazine pages. Packages such as Microsoft Publisher can also be used to help produce your presentation boards. Blocks of text and images can be moved and manipulated to produce interesting effects and a variety of layouts.

DTP is also used to import images from a variety of sources and other packages. A scanned image or a picture from a camera can be imported into the program and used.

Programs such as Adobe Illustrator®, Photoshop® and CorelDraw® can be used to work on original artwork. Textures, colours and effects can be added to help develop your final image.

A 3D product can be designed in a CAD package like Pro/DESKTOP, Pro/ENGINEER, SolidWorks or Google SketchUp. The design is generated in a 3D form that can be viewed from any angle.

- o The image can be **photo-rendered** to give an accurate impression of what the product will look like.
- o Texture and material selection is used to help visualise the product as it would be manufactured.

△ **Figure 4.36** This illustrates how a 3D CAD package can be used to render, model, manufacture and produce workshop-dimensioned drawings

The design can be quickly converted into an orthographic drawing, then dimensioned to help third-party manufacture. The design can then be output onto a CNC router or rapid prototyping machine. This will give an accurate solid three-dimensional form to the item.

Encapsulation

To help protect finished design sheets, work can be **encapsulated**. Encapsulation coats both sides of the presentation in plastic. Desktop laminating devices are used in some schools. Paper or thin card is placed into a plastic pocket and inserted between heated rollers. This heat pressing seals around the product. Once encapsulated, the graphic will be water-resistant and can be used as a write-on, wipe-off surface.

Digital presentation

Your work can be presented in a digital format. This could be useful for interviews, or as a submission to your teacher or a client. A good format for this type of presentation is Microsoft PowerPoint®.

PowerPoint® is an easy way to sequence and show your work. Not all of your project will be completed on the computer, but it would need to be scanned, or photographed to drop into the slide show.

Some problems may occur:

1. The file size can be large. You might need to look at ways of reducing the scanned and photographed images. Some quality will be lost in doing this, but it will make the process more manageable.

2. Scanning and photographing work take time. Allow for this, and also for the sizing and positioning within the document.

> ## Exam tip
> A great temptation is to add lots of effects with images swirling in and letters marching across the screen one at a time. Try to avoid this; keep it simple so that the viewer can skip to the relevant parts easily.

A contents page can be set up at the start of the slideshow. This can be linked to hyperlinks, or slides further into the presentation. For example, if you want to jump to the final design page, this can be done quickly and easily with a click of the mouse.

4.7 Pictorial drawings

One-point perspective

The further away an object is, the smaller it appears to be. This is easiest to see on a straight part of motorway, or a street which is lined with trees or has lamp posts at regular intervals.

Drawing by hand in one-point perspective is a very useful method for showing rooms.

Activities

Make a sketch of your room.

1. Always put in the horizontal line, or eye level, first. Create a square using only horizontal and vertical lines which will serve as the back of your room. Select a point on the eye level which will be the vanishing point; see Figure 4.37.
2. Add the diagonals; see Figure 4.38.
3. Add the ceiling, walls and floor. Keep the verticals and horizontal lines parallel to the edges of the paper; see Figure 4.39.
4. Add the following:
   ○ a window
   ○ a door
   ○ a bed.

Try to add these where they are in your room, or copy the drawing. When you have done this, add objects of your choice, such as a computer table or desk and a rug; see Figure 4.40.

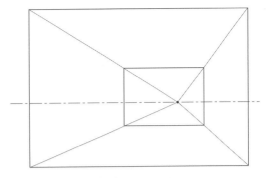

△ **Figure 4.39** Back of room, eye level, diagonals and square of room

Key points

Vertical and horizontal lines are parallel to the edges of the paper.

The front surface of the object is drawn flat.

Key terms

Vanishing point – the point where the lines seem to disappear.

Eye level – the level of the viewer.

Two-point perspective

For a more realistic image, it is best to use two-point perspective.

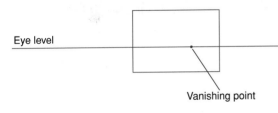

△ **Figure 4.37** Back of room and eye level

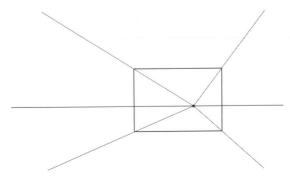

△ **Figure 4.38** Back of room, eye level and diagonals

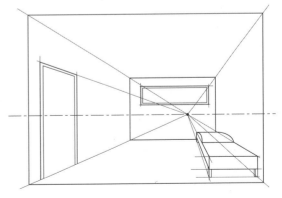

△ **Figure 4.40** Perspective with doorway, bed and window added

Activities

1. Draw the horizontal line or eye level. For the first example, look from above, as well as from the front and side of the object.

2. Put two vanishing points on the page, ensuring that they are in line horizontally and near the edge of the page. Create a box or crate. Make the box to one side of the middle. See Figure 4.41.

3. On the front face of the box, create your first initial. Make it into 3D. Complete the drawing by adding all of your initials. Some boxes will need to be bigger than others; an 'M' will take up more space than a 'Y' or 'C'. Some letters will not be easy, so plan out the spacing on the front face first! See Figure 4.42.

4. If the eye level is below the object, the bottom will be seen. See Figure 4.43.

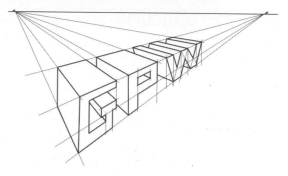

△ **Figure 4.42** Two-point perspective: outline of initials

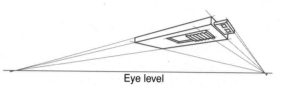

△ **Figure 4.43** Two-point perspective of USB

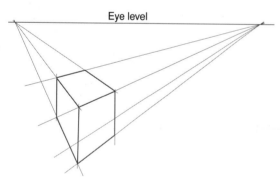

△ **Figure 4.41** Two-point perspective: initial outline of box or crate

Exam tip

Look at the work of Giovanni Antonio Canal (1697–1768), better known as Canaletto. He was a Venetian painter, famous for his landscapes. The level of detail and the use of two-point perspective are superb. Try printing out a copy of one of his scenes (black and white is good enough!) and add the lines to the vanishing points to see how he has achieved the perspective.

Key points

You do not have to draw all of the guidelines to the vanishing points. If you do this every time, the work can become muddled and dirty.

There are some very good perspective software packages available on the internet, which can be used to achieve lifelike drawings. Adobe Illustrator and Google SketchUp work very well.

Isometric sketching

Isometric sketches can be very accurate. You must ensure that the side and end are drawn at 30 degrees to the horizontal for very accurate work. Use gridded paper behind your sheet of paper to get the best results when sketching freehand. It will show through and give guidelines for your work.

You can use the actual sizes of the object. Figure 4.44 shows how a cube would be shown.

Key points
○ Lines which are vertical on the object will be vertical on the drawing.
○ Lines that are horizontal on the object will be at 30 degrees on the drawing.
○ All measurements are actual size.

For the best results, it is easiest to put a box around any object that you need to draw. Treat your shape as a piece of cheese that you remove part from, or add to, to achieve the final form. Figure 4.46 shows a series of stages in creating a variety of shapes.

To create a circle in isometric, use the box and the centre lines together. The shape you see and draw will actually be an ellipse. It is also possible to use an ellipse template, but you will need a range of these for the shapes you are going to need. The sketch in Figure 4.45 shows the stages in the construction of the ellipse.

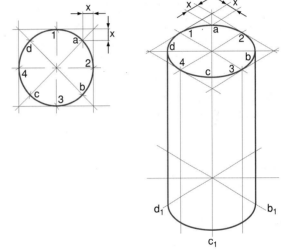

△ **Figure 4.45** Drawing a circle in isometric

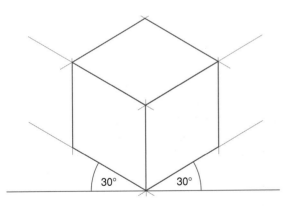

△ **Figure 4.44** Isometric view of a cube

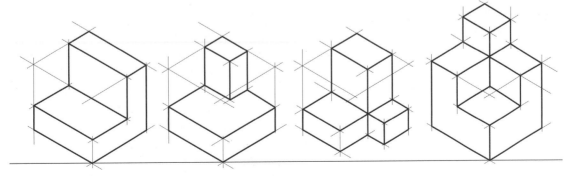

△ **Figure 4.46** Construction by wasting or adding to the boxed shape

57

Drawing the plan view means you can get all of the sizes from your circle, but you only **need** to draw one quarter of the circle to save time and effort, and then repeat the markings four times. If your circle is very big you will need to take more than just the distance X to draw it accurately. You can use the same measuring in from the corners method if you are drawing a shape which is an ellipse in plan view, like the top of some tissue boxes.

Activity

Using an object such as a deodorant can, straight-sided mug or lipstick tube, make an isometric sketch of the shape. As it is the first example, keep the shape simple, but when you have understood the technique, create a more complicated form. Add the detail such as the brand name and the information on the outside.

Figure 4.47 shows the first stages of a drawing for a soap dispenser. Look at how the centre lines are used, along with the crating (see section 4.4). Gentle curves can be rounded off, and there is no firm outline at this stage; that will be drawn in when the shape is clear.

Key terms

Centre lines – chain lines which run through the middle of your work or circles.

Ellipse template – transparent plastic with elliptical shapes cut out to act as guides.

Isometric grid – lines on a paper at 30 degrees, used as a guide.

△ **Figure 4.47** Drawing of a soap dispenser in isometric

4.8 Working drawings

What is a working drawing?

A working drawing is the final 'constructed' drawing, produced as part of the design process. It usually consists of a front, side and plan view of the product. The designer can choose how many views to draw, and this will depend on the complexity of the ideas to be drawn. Sizes or 'dimensions' are added so that any person using the working drawing can manufacture the product. The designer can add as much information as is required for the manufacturer to make the product.

A working drawings must be precise and can be drawn to a scale. The scale must be appropriate to the task and the needs of both designer and producer. If the drawing needs to show the product at half its proper size, then the scale is said to be 1:2.

Working drawings can be constructed on the drawing board using drawing instruments or by using a Computer-Aided Design (CAD) system. Drawings should be understood by all the users, and British standards are produced for most cases to allow designers to communicate ideas technically with the producers and manufacturers.

Using third-angle orthographic projection

Orthographic projection is one form of working drawing. Third-angle orthographic projection is used to show details and sizes of a designed object or product and it usually requires three views (front, side and plan) with sizes or dimensions, usually in millimetres.

Drawings are produced to a British Standard BS8888, 2006, so that anyone can understand and interpret the information on the drawing. Orthographic means 'drawing at right angles', and this is a two-dimensional (2D) method of drawing products or objects.

Third-angle or American orthographic projection is the most common method of producing a working drawing. A drawing is constructed by producing the following:

1. front view: produced by looking at the front of a product.

2. plan view: drawn directly above the front view. Sometimes incorrectly referred to as the 'bird's eye view'.

3. end/side view: drawn by looking at the end or side of a product. Usually shows the most detail.

Orthographic drawings are used for production purposes, so the drawing should contain enough detail in the form of dimensions to enable a third party or manufacturer to make the product. As a designer, you will need to produce a working drawing for the outcome or three-dimensional (3D) object which you will design for the GCSE coursework. The working drawing will help to manufacture your product, and it may need to be drawn to scale.

Activities

Produce a third-angle orthographic drawing.

1. Start with the largest side first, which is usually the front view. Draw construction lines for the front view. Project these lines up, to enable you to produce your plan view (above). Project lines across so that you can construct your side or end view (to the side).

2. **Hidden detail:** drawn as a series of short dashes using thin lines. Any lines you cannot directly see but you know exist (such as the inside of the mug) are drawn in Figure 4.48.

△ **Figure 4.48** Using hidden detail

Dimensioning working drawings

Measurements are added to the working drawing so that the manufacturer can make the object or product to the right size; this is called dimensioning. It is important that the dimensions are drawn so that:

1. The sizes can be easily read and understood.

2. A leader line should not touch the object outline.

3. All measurements can be read from the bottom right-hand side of the drawing.

4. Sizes should be written above each dimension line and arrows at each end.

5. Sizes should be in millimetres (include this information on the drawing).

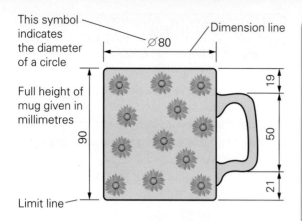

This symbol indicates the diameter of a circle

⌀80

Dimension line

Full height of mug given in millimetres

90

19

50

21

Limit line

△ **Figure 4.49** Adding dimensioning to a drawing

An example of correct dimensioning technique is shown in Figure 4.49. Figure 4.50 shows the correct British Standard methods for adding dimensions to features such as the radius of curves, small sizes, angles and circles.

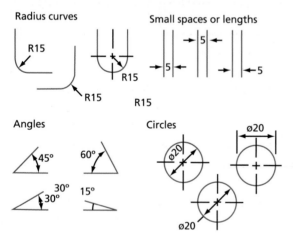

Radius curves

R15

R15

R15

R15

Small spaces or lengths

5

5

5

Angles

45°

60°

30°
30°

15°

Circles

⌀20

⌀20

⌀20

⌀20

△ **Figure 4.50** Correct dimensioning methods

> ### Key terms
>
> **Dimensions** – sizes, usually in millimetres (mm).
>
> **Third-angle orthographic projection** – a standard technique for producing detailed working drawings that everyone can understand.
>
> **Front view** – a view looking at the front of your product.
>
> **Plan view** – a view looking down at the top of your product.
>
> **End/side view** – a view looking at the end or side of your product.
>
> **Hidden detail** – lines you cannot directly see but which you know exist.

Self-assembly, sectional and exploded drawings

Understand the use of self-assembly

Assembly drawings are used when the many parts of a product come together and are assembled in a correct order to form the finished product. Self-assembly products are produced by a company in pieces and sold as 'flat packs', with detailed instructions for the purchaser so that they can put the item together. Companies such as IKEA® or Airfix would not allow their customers to assemble the products without good-quality, easy-to-read assembly instructions. Self-assembly products are usually drawn in 3D because research has found that most people find such drawings easier to visualise and therefore understand.

1. Cut out the pieces.
2. Glue together both sides of the fuselage wings and tailplane.
3. Cut out the slots for the wing and tailplane.
4. Curve each engine into a cylinder and glue along the shaded area.
5. Slot in the wing and tailplane and attach the engines with glue in the positions indicated.

Engines

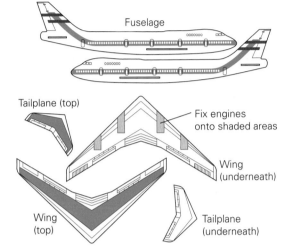

Fuselage

Tailplane (top)

Fix engines onto shaded areas

Wing (underneath)

Wing (top)

Tailplane (underneath)

△ **Figure 4.51** Orthographic view of the parts required for a model plane

A well-drawn assembly drawing can save a thousand words of explanation. Self-assembly instructions usually contain very few words – all the information is pictorial. Instructions should always include a list of parts which will inform the customer of what is in the package. This information can be graphical and show drawings of the parts, or in the form of a table listing the parts; finally the instructions should show a step-by-step method of making the product which is clear and easy to understand.

Self assembly can have benefits for all the users:

1. A company can store many more products (flat-pack furniture or model parts) in a certain space, and thereby save money on storage warehousing.
2. Customers pay a lower price for the product because the company has not had to pay for skilled final assembly.

3. Instructions drawn in 3D are generally printed on recycled low-quality paper, which is also better for the environment.

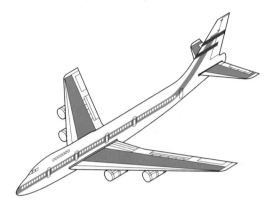

△ **Figure 4.52** Assembly drawing of model plane

Activity

Can you think of any disadvantages of self-assembly drawings?

Key terms

Self-assembly – independently constructing an item from a kit using instructions supplied.

Parts list – details such as size, materials, number, etc., about each part that makes up the product.

Assemble – put together.

Understand the use of sectional drawings

Sectional drawings are ones which show the inside of an object as if it was cut open. For example, sectional drawings could be used to represent what a chocolate bar would look like inside if it was cut open; see Figure 4.53.

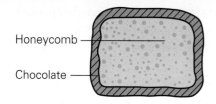

Honeycomb

Chocolate

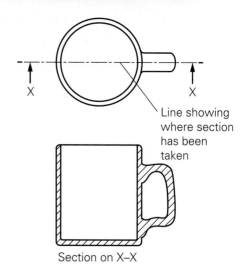

X   X

Line showing where section has been taken

Wafer biscuit

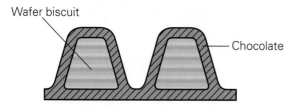

Chocolate

Section on X–X

△ **Figure 4.53** Sectional views of chocolate bars

You can cut the object into sections in one of many ways; for example, you can cut it along its length, which would produce a helpful sectional drawing of the outline of the chocolate and the honeycomb inside.

The technique of cutting objects open is called **sectioning**. The areas where the object is cut are shown by **hatching**. This is made up of lines usually drawn at 45 degrees; usually a different direction of hatching for each part of the assembled object. Sectional drawing can use a very complex technique, but doing so allows the drawing to show internal details, which will help the manufacturer understand the product.

Making a sectional drawing

Imagine cutting through a ceramic mug with a saw. What would you see? Why would you want to see inside an object?

See Figure 4.54: a line is drawn across the view you want to section, and arrows are then added in the direction of the view you want to produce. These arrows are labelled, starting with the first section line labelled X-X in this case.

Imagine that when the saw cuts through the surface of the mug, a hatch line is produced on the sectional drawing where it makes contact with the object. The hatch lines are usually at

△ **Figure 4.54** Producing a drawing which includes a sectional view

45 degrees, and equally spaced. Where the saw does not touch the surface of the object, the area is left blank – not hatched.

Key terms

Sectional drawing – a drawing produced by cutting through an object.

Hatching – equally spaced lines, usually drawn at 45 degrees, which represent where an object has been sectioned.

Demonstrate the use of exploded drawings

Exploded drawings are 3D drawings which show how an object has been constructed. Sections of the object are drawn separately from one another but remain in relation to each other.

A client may ask a manufacturer to produce a package for a high-quality video game, and to show how the flat-pack product could be assembled on the production line. An exploded drawing would be included in the instructional booklet to show the manufacturer how to construct the product.

In Figure 4.55 we can see an exploded view of the packaging for the video game. Each part is related to how all parts of the package will be assembled.

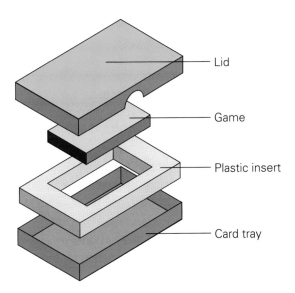

Lid

Game

Plastic insert

Card tray

△ **Figure 4.55** Exploded view of the packaging for a video game

Use and understand scale drawings

If possible, it is always better to draw an object in its full size. A scale drawing is used when it is impractical to draw the product at its real size because it is too big to fit on a single sheet of paper, or too small to be understood with ease. To enable the drawing of the product to be seen and easily comprehended, a scale is used. Scale is understood to be a ratio and therefore has no units; it is shown as 1:2, 1:50, etc. The scale is the ratio between the drawing and the object, not the other way round. For example, a scale of 1:2 indicates that the drawing is half the size of the object.

It is very important to remember that the actual size/dimension still needs to be on the scaled drawing; do not put the size as the length of the line on the paper. As a quality control check, the person reading the drawing should be able to measure a line and then multiply it by the scale to get the actual size.

An example of an object that is better viewed full size is a postage stamp, but some detail of the drawing may not be clear. Drawing the stamp twice its full size can make the detail easier to view.

◁ **Figure 4.56** Full-sized drawing of a postage stamp

◁ **Figure 4.57** Enlarged view of a postage stamp

A building plan or maps are examples of designs that should be drawn smaller to allow the practical use of the product. Maps drawn full size would be impractical, and scales of above 1:1,000 are often used.

Key term

Scale – the ratio between the drawing and the object.

Know how to interpret room or site plans and maps

Room or floor plans are scaled-down drawings used by architects and designers to show exactly how the inside of a new building is to be constructed, or how an existing one is laid out. Plans will be detailed enough to show where doors, windows and positions of other features are shown, allowing other people to understand how the space inside a building is to be used. After construction, interior designers will modify the drawings to include furniture and lighting.

Schematic drawings are produced for a specific practical function, usually electrical wiring layout or central heating distribution. For example:

o An electrician will use a schematic drawing to illustrate the power lines and to show where the electricity cables enter a building; the information will be shared with the interior designer so that sockets and lighting are installed in the correct places.

o A plumber may use a different schematic drawing showing the location of the water supply and sewerage pipes to the building. This will assist the siting of bathrooms and installation of central heating.

Site plans are drawings which show a project site from an aerial view. When a builder is building a new street, site plans are used to represent where each of the houses will be built. The plans could be submitted as part of the planning permission process by local councils, such as at public meetings before building begins, to gauge opinion on the plans. Sales staff use site plans to show potential buyers where their house will be situated and what it will look like when it is built.

A map is simply a plan of the ground on paper. The plan is usually drawn as the land would be seen from directly above. A map will normally have the following features:

o the names of important places and locations

o standard symbols to show the location of key landmarks and features

o a key, or a legend, to explain what the symbols on the map mean

o a scale and scale bar to allow you to measure distance on the map and convert it to the actual distance on the land

o a grid system of lines to allow you to pinpoint your location, orientate your map to the land and quickly estimate distances

o contour lines to show relief (the height of the ground above sea level) and the steepness of the land.

Let's say for example that a customer has chosen to promote a computer game at a national convention centre.

o After the promotion stand has been successfully designed, the designer must produce a package of information for the customer.

o The game will be promoted at a national convention centre. Maps must be produced to show the company's clients and visitors how to get there.

o A site plan will show the location of the stand in the convention centre.

o A floor plan will inform the stand builders of what to build on the site.

o Services to the stand such as lighting and power must be drawn as a schematic for the electricians to understand.

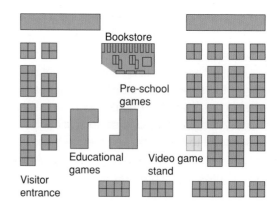

△ **Figure 4.58** Drawings and maps used to promote a video game

The successful video games promotion will depend on people interpreting floor, sites and schematic plans and successfully understanding maps.

Exam tip

You may be asked to draw a surface development to a scale of 1:2 in an exam. Remember that even though you can draw it half scale, you must still add the actual size next to it.

4.9 Surface (net) development

Knowledge link

For more information on surface development, see Chapter 11.

The majority of products are packaged in some way. The function of the packaging is to protect, preserve, contain and inform. The imagery on the packaging will also help to improve the appearance, increase sales, develop brand awareness and create a familiarity, which is important for both the consumer and the manufacturer.

Packaging therefore is very important, especially the amount of packaging used. The best type of packaging will be capable of reuse. A milk bottle made from glass is an excellent package which can be reused many times. If the package cannot be reused, then it is best if it can be recycled. Milk in a carton made from HDPE can be recycled, but will require three important steps:

1. The carton must be coded with a '2' in the middle of a recycle triangle.
2. The user must selectively dispose of the carton.
3. The carton must be sorted for recycling at the collection point.

HDPE

◁ **Figure 4.59**
A recycle triangle

Manufacturing 3D containers from sheet material

Making a 3D form from a 2D shape means that the outline must be drawn accurately. Figure 4.60 shows two cartons which are very familiar; both have simple developments.

Activity

Make a drawing of the development for both boxes in Figure 4.60.

Important: look closely at the ways in which the lids or openings work. The locking tab and glued surfaces are positioned for best effect. Add these details to your development.

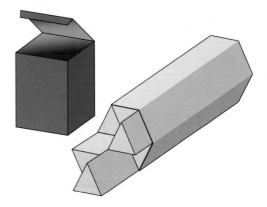

△ **Figure 4.60** Familiar cartons with simple developments

The development of a cylinder

The development of a **cylinder** is no more complicated, especially if it is just for a label similar to those on a baked bean can.

△ **Figure 4.61** A cylinder

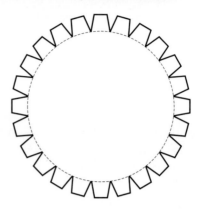

△ **Figure 4.63** A base for the cylinder

> ### Activity
> Draw a line the same length as the circumference of the baked bean can. Add the height and create a rectangle the same size as the label. It can also be done by drawing as in Figure 4.62, although this is not quite as accurate.

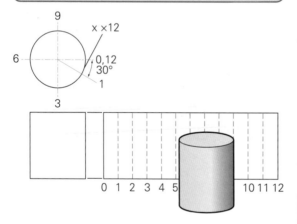

△ **Figure 4.62** The development of a cylinder

The shape in Figure 4.63 shows what a base would look like if you were to draw an end for the cylinder. Note how all the tabs would have to be bent upwards individually, ready to be stuck to the sides.

> ### Key points
> o Accuracy is vital for the best possible results. Small mistakes made with the compass can be exaggerated when stepped off 12 times.
> o Always number or letter the parts to make sure that your work is accurate.

The development of a cone and pyramid

To draw the development of a **cone**, it is necessary to draw a front view and a plan. This will mean that in the side view, the side of the cone is a true length (actual length of the side and not foreshortened by the angle). Later when drawing a pyramid, it will be essential that the side of the shape is a true length. Always check you are working with true lengths.

> ### Activity
> Draw the plan and side elevation of the cone. It will need to be about 80 mm diameter and 100 mm high. On the side view, imagine that the cone rolls out without slipping. At the same time as it is rolling around, it is also unravelling. The shape shown in Figure 4.64 will be the shape of the cone when developed. It is important to make sure that the development has 12 equal sectors, so number your development from 0 to 12.

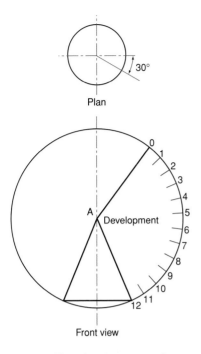

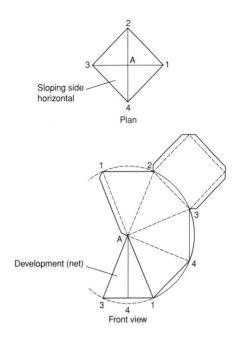

△ **Figure 4.64** The development of a cone

△ **Figure 4.65** The development of a pyramid

 Activity

To develop a **pyramid**, use the same technique as with the cone.

Draw the plan and side elevation of the pyramid. The sizes can be about the same as the cone to make it easier to draw. Make sure that the edge in the side view is a true length. On the side view, imagine that the pyramid is unfolded without slipping. The shape shown in Figure 4.65 will be the shape of the pyramid when developed. In this case, it is important to make sure that the development has *four* equal triangles, so number your development as is shown.

A base has been added, along with some glue tabs. Make sure when you cut it out that you leave the tabs in place and crease the fold lines. A good way to put creases in this sort of work is to use a biro that no longer has any ink in it, and to go over the lines. This technique will break the fibres of the paper and create a weakness along the lines before they are folded.

The same technique can be used for any based pyramid, whether it has three or more sides. This is the foundation of all development work.

The majority of packaging can be created using the techniques already covered, but it is important that the package has a bottom and in some cases a top which fixes together.

Figure 4.66 shows a lunchbox for children which is supplied by the National Trust. It has not only a tab lock lid, but also a two-spot glued base which is a crash pattern.

△ **Figure 4.66** A children's lunchbox, supplied by the National Trust

Activity

Collect five types of boxes where the bases are of a different shape. Start with a cereal carton and a packet of tea, and carefully unfold three more. Make a drawing of the types of bases on each of the packages. Give a reason for the base being constructed in the way it is; for example, a bottle carrier would be more substantial than a perfume box because of the weight going inside the box.

Key terms

Tab – small projecting surface of material.

True length – length of the side which is not foreshortened by the angle.

Plan view – when drawn looking from above; sometimes called a bird's eye view.

Surface detail – lettering and images on the product (must be the right way up).

Using CAD and CAM to produce and manipulate surface development

For the drawing and cutting out of a development in CAD, it is essential for the software to be capable of interacting with both computer and cutter. This is best performed using Techsoft or a similar software package, and the vinyl cutter. This equipment is still relatively expensive, and not all centres will have one of their own. The production and manipulation of a development by CAM can be even more expensive. If your centre does not own these facilities, it is worth looking up the techniques on the internet. A short video will make the processes very clear. However, this next series of figures will help you to gain a good understanding.

Using a forme press

Cutting out the 2D packaging by hand can be a long job. By machine it is a relatively quick process, once it has been set up. Figure 4.67 is a photo showing an operator using a forme press to cut out many shapes all at the same time. The forme is described in Chapter 11.

Notice how the shape being cut out is repeated on the forme. This means that many of the shapes can be cut at one press. The outline of the forme will have been determined using CAD.

△ **Figure 4.67** Using a forme cutting machine

Vinyl cutter

As well as being able to use the forme for cutting out the development, it is possible to use a vinyl cutter (see also Chapter 11). The operator should ensure that the vinyl is being fed squarely into the cutter as the tool traces out the shape of the development, cutting as it goes. The profile of the tool must be kept sharp to avoid damaging the surface of the vinyl. The cutter will determine precise shapes every time, giving accurate results and working very quickly. A Computer Numerically Controlled (CNC) machine is used to cut out a development in a resistant material. Figure 4.69 shows acrylic being cut out by this technique, ready to be bent and finished before assembling as part of a point-of-sale display.

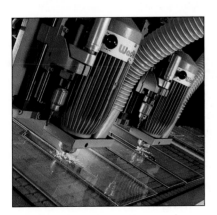

△ **Figure 4.68** Ensure that the feed is not creased

△ **Figure 4.69** A CNC machine cutting acrylic

Line bending

Figure 4.70 shows a line bender for the acrylic. It is similar to the type of line bender used in examination centres, but in this case it is much bigger. A heating element warms the acrylic at the exact point it is to be bent, and the machine pulls it into position.

△ **Figure 4.70** A line bending machine

When the acrylic has been bent to shape, it is finished using a flame. This is possible because of the quality of the finish from the CNC machine.

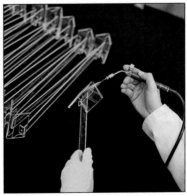

△ **Figure 4.71** A flame polishes the acrylic edges

Key points
o Preparing for machine-made products takes time to set up and is expensive.
o Producing high volumes of products increases the efficiency and reduces costs.

4.10 Information drawing

Represent data in graphic form

What is graphical representation of data?

The graphic designer sometimes needs to gather information and then display that data in an understandable way. For ease of understanding, the numerical result is usually converted into a graphical form, either by drawing graphs by hand or using a spreadsheet application such as Microsoft Excel®; the data can then be presented in Microsoft PowerPoint®. When data is collected, it needs to be accurately collated, analysed and presented in a form that is fair and truthful. Putting the numbers into a table can make it very hard to interpret, and it is the job of the graphic designer to make the information interesting and accessible.

Data can be presented in a variety of ways:

1. pie charts
2. bar charts
3. pictographs
4. line graphs.

Pie charts

Pie charts are used when proportions within the data need to be shown. This type of data representation is used if you want to show, for example, how many people in your class used different types of transport to get to school. You may want to show the different types as fractions of the whole class.

The area of the pie is calculated by using the following formula, and then the data is drawn on the chart using a protractor. In this way, the data is converted into fractions of the total; sectors of the circle look like slices of a pie.

Formula

On the pie chart, the total number of degrees should add up to 360. Each sector should be clearly labelled or colour-coded (show key to coding) to show the amount of data, or it will not be clear what each of the sectors is representing. Sectors or slices with a different contrasting colour will add to the visual impact of this type of chart.

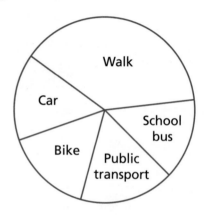

△ **Figure 4.72** A pie chart

Bar charts

Bar charts are used for showing direct visual comparisons between data. The chart shows the relative size of each category of data; this is useful when you are trying to show the results from a questionnaire, where the data shows preferences for a particular colour or product.

Bar charts are drawn in many different ways, but mainly with the bars vertically or horizontally. How you draw the chart is up to you. All axes and information should be clearly labelled.

Microsoft Excel® is particularly efficient when creating a chart; using the 'tools', it is possible to design a chart to suit most data representation needs.

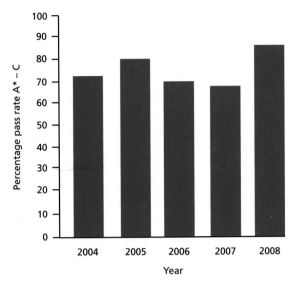

△ **Figure 4.73** A bar chart

When drawing a line graph, make sure that the **constant** data (such as months) is displayed along the horizontal axis, while the **variable** data (such as sales figures) is displayed on the vertical axis.

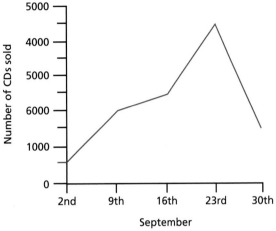

△ **Figure 4.75** A line graph

Pictographs

Pictographs are similar to bar charts but use symbols or pictures to represent the data. This can be easier to understand, because the symbols and pictures show what the data means. The difficulty with pictographs is that the data could use different graphics for different values, and it is important that the overall value of each graphic remains the same.

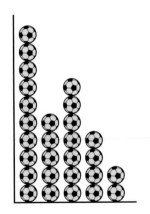
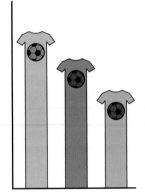

△ **Figure 4.74** A pictograph

Line graphs

Line graphs are used to show changes in data. In hospital, changes in patient temperature are sometimes recorded every hour using a line graph.

Activity

Design a survey for your class using the following questions to gather data:

o How do you travel to school or college in the mornings?
o What is your favourite colour?

Design appropriate graphs to display the data.

Exam tip

DO NOT include every diagram and chart you know of in the controlled assessment. For information graphics, marks are awarded for accuracy and colour quality.

Understanding and drawing graphs will usually form part of the examination.

Understand the language of signs and labels

Signs

How do we understand what signs are trying to tell us? Signs are there to give us instructions or warnings. The best examples are road signs warning us of such things as a slippery road, or how to find a place of local interest. Signs may include a symbol or graphic to help the public understand what the sign is trying to communicate, although this also acts as a method of informing people who are not able to understand the language in which it is written, such as a tourist from abroad.

Signs must be clear and eye-catching so that they can easily be seen and understood. The symbols that are used on most common road signs are called **pictograms**, and many of these are instantly recognisable throughout the world. A good example of this is the sign that warns the public of the location of a school, or where children may be crossing the road. The signs shown in Figure 4.75 were designed by Jock Kinnear (see Chapter 3 for more information).

△ **Figure 4.76** Examples of road signs

Labels

Labels explain to the consumer information about the product. They may also tell the consumer how to use it or care for it, in the form of a leaflet or as part of the packaging. Good labelling should give the purchaser clear information on the material used in the packaging and the product, and additional useful data such as how to dispose of the item and recycle it safely.

One of the most important areas of labelling in graphic design is the selling and packaging of food products. It is a legal requirement to label all packaged food (but not loose food such as fresh meats and vegetables) with information that includes the following:

○ the name of the food
○ nutritional information, such as the amount of salt and fat per 100 g
○ preparation and cooking instructions
○ the storage instructions including the 'best before' and 'use by' dates
○ a list of any special claims and warnings, for example contents linked to food allergies
○ a list of the ingredients, starting with the largest or main ingredient
○ the weight or volume of the product, sometimes represented as 'e' which means 'estimated'
○ the name and address of the manufacturer or seller.

Symbols can be used as instructions to make them easier to understand, such as symbols for freezing and cooking.

Washing instructions are found on clothes labels to help the purchaser understand when and how the garments should be cleaned. Symbols are used to represent instructions such as washing and ironing temperatures.

Quality and standards labels can be attached to products where they apply. The Kitemark indicates British Standards, and the CE mark is used to show that the product can be sold anywhere in the European Union.

△ **Figure 4.77** Label on food product

△ **Figure 4.78** A barcode

Barcodes

Most products sold in the UK now carry a barcode as part of the label or package. The retailer uses the barcode in many ways: the name and price of the product are registered at the till or point of sale by scanning with the barcode reader. The point-of-sale device will automatically enter the purchase details on the receipt, and can inform the retailer as to which products sell the most or least items.

Data collected from the scanning of barcodes can be used to help the retailer control the amount of product in the warehouse and the reordering of items to keep the shop shelves stocked. Barcodes are used on loyalty cards to collect information on shopping habits. The information can help stores to target products to advertise to individual shoppers.

The function and use of corporate identity

Corporate identity means giving a graphical identity to a company; designers create visual images that make the consumer think of the company. When companies want to be remembered in a visual way, they will ask graphic designers to create an image that will be understood quickly and clearly.

A corporate identity is about far more than just a logo. Once an organisation has agreed its corporate identity, it will want to ensure that it is widely adopted, and not just an isolated logo on notepaper.

Corporate identity should tell the customers what they are likely to expect from the company.

Logos

Logos create an impression of the company and the quality of the services provided or the products produced. Big or small organisations can use a logo to make sure that consumers recognise their identity.

When designing a company logo, the graphic designer considers the many parts of the organisation such as existing advertising, location, the company name, the image which the company wants to project, etc. All the elements of the organisation may be combined into the design of a simple logo, which presents the face of the company.

△ **Figure 4.79** Company logo

Designers must take many factors into consideration when designing a logo for a company. For example:

o The logo must be clear and eye-catching. How can this be achieved – through strong colours and interesting shapes? Can the logo be used as a trademark?

o The design must be usable across a range of media. Will it look good on a letter heading, an advertising billboard, on the side of company vehicles, etc.?

Activity

Produce a new corporate identity logo for your school or college.

Key terms

Trademark – unique mark that helps to identify a product.

Corporate identity – colours, images and slogans that help the consumer to recognise a company.

Logo – an image associated with an organisation.

Logogram – a logo which uses the initial letters of an organisation, such as NHS (National Health Service).

Logotypes – a logo which uses a different font, such as British Airways.

Exam tip

Understand the elements which make an effective corporate identity.

Produce symbols, ideograms and pictograms

KEEP BRITAIN TIDY

◁ **Figure 4.80** Example of a symbol

Symbol production

Symbols are produced either to communicate information as instructions or to aid recognition of the product. Symbols are produced as:

o abstract – symbols which portray a concept which people can recognise. For example, the five Olympic rings represent the five continents of the world.

- action – such as the road sign showing a worker digging: this is used to warn drivers about road works.
- pictorial – also called pictograms, these are simple pictures used to inform the public; for example, signs indicating events at the Olympic Games.

The main reason to produce symbols is to provide visual information, so that most people can quickly understand what the designer is trying to tell us.

Ideograms production

Ideograms are produced by creating simple pictures which communicate a message. Early cave dwellers showed each other through cave painting how to hunt animals.

An ideogram informs the viewer without the need for written explanation. For example, if we see a sign showing a bicycle, we will assume that it means a cycle track; if there is a sign with a bed, we may assume that nearby is a property which rents rooms.

◁ **Figure 4.81** Example of an ideogram

Pictograms production

Pictograms have a similar purpose to ideograms, but are usually simpler in their design. Block drawing is used with contrasting colours and they are completely wordless, which eliminates the need for people to be able to read in a particular language in order to understand the information presented. Pictograms convey information to the general public.

Pictograms are used on packaging to describe how the package or the product should be used. Recycling pictograms can explain how the materials can be reused.

△ **Figure 4.82** Examples of pictograms

Exam tip

Producing symbols and pictograms designed for purpose is an activity in the exam.

Key terms

Symbols – visual devices used to communicate.

Ideograms – pictorial symbols used to communicate a message.

Pictograms – simple ideograms without language and used in public places.

Activity

Look at the instructions on the side of a packet of washing powder, and try to work out each stage in the process.

Produce flowcharts with feedback loops

Flowchart

A flowchart is a good way of illustrating a sequence of operations that need to be undertaken when doing a task such as making a product or fixing a device. It can be used to find a fault and show how to repair it – this is sometimes called a **diagnostic tool**. Flowcharts are produced using standardised symbols, with arrows showing the direction in which you should follow the flow of the operations.

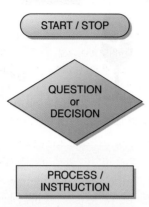

△ **Figure 4.83** Flowchart symbols with descriptions

Figure 4.84 shows a flowchart of a production planning process. Follow the arrows to see what you have to do next. Charts are used to check that all tasks are complete, no task has been missed out and the sequence of the activities is correct. Decision symbols show what will result in a yes or no answer, and a loop can be put into the system. This is called a **feedback loop**.

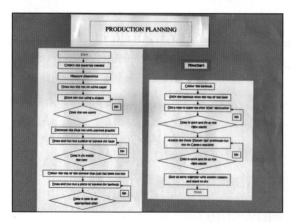

△ **Figure 4.84** Example of a flowchart

Depending on the answer, the flow may either continue straight on, or 'loop' back to a previous stage, in which case a decision or event must take place to move forward. In the chart, the operator is asked to make a decision about the type of disc. If the disc is not correct, the operator will go back and input the data before the sequence can move forward.

Flowchart guidelines

o Flowcharts can easily be produced on a computer using the new MS Office suite. All flowchart shapes are in the drawing area of the program.
o Sketch out your flowchart to check that it works.
o Draw the flowcharts downwards or from left to right.
o Use arrows to indicate the direction of 'flow'.

Activity

Work out the inputs, processes and output including feedback for the following activities:

o making a cup of tea
o recording a television programme.

Key terms

Flowchart – drawing which explains the sequence of an operation, showing inputs, processes and outputs.

Inputs – information or materials which are part of the sequence.

Process – what is done in the flowchart.

Outputs – the final outcomes of the flowchart.

Feedback – information for the user on what is happening during the process.

Operations – individual processes and functions.

Operator – the person who is controlling the process.

Feedback loop –part of a flowchart showing the operator which stage to return to if necessary.

Sequential illustrations and schematic maps

Sequential illustrations

Sequential illustrations are a series of drawings showing the steps in a process of production. Flat-pack furniture companies such as IKEA® produce excellent sequential illustrations, showing the purchasers how the goods can be put together. Airfix kits have extensive drawings, showing the maker how to construct very complex models of vehicles and aircraft, step by step.

Designers must ensure that the diagrams are easy to understand and clearly explain visually every step of production by ensuring that they:

o produce clear outline drawings which need not be coloured or rendered
o are drawn in 3D to a scale that is easy to read
o are sequenced with numbers to help the reader follow instructions
o keep written instructions to a minimum and use arrows to link the words with the drawing.

Schematic maps

Schematic maps are produced to show the connection between places, but they do not try to represent the distances between the places or the accurate geographical location. An example of a schematic map is the London Underground. All tube lines are shown and are linked together on coloured straight lines. The designer Harry Beck produced this map to make easier the task of getting around London on the Underground (see Chapter 3 for more information).

Schematic maps show routes using major roads with intersections, roundabouts, stations and points of interest along the route. Advertisers and information services use the schematic map as a guide to schools and shopping malls, and also for tours around local attractions.

Key term

Sequential illustrations – step-by-step drawings to show the process of making something.

Summary

o You should model your ideas quickly, using available materials.
o CAD is an excellent way of communicating an idea.
o Be able to communicate a concept to a potential client, manufacturer or purchaser.
o Know the functions of mock-ups, models and prototypes, and the important role which they can play in the design process.

o A target market is the group of people at which your design idea is aimed.
o A gap in the market is where a product does not exist to meet the needs of the consumer.
o Sketching allows you to develop your ideas and allows others to understand them.
o Enhancement techniques such as shape, proportion, pattern, texture and colour allow the designer to represent the aesthetic in their sketching and block models and give the product its look and style. *Cont.*

Summary *continued*

o The presentation of your work is very important. Your design folder should contain a range of imaginative ideas, with clear annotation referencing materials, manufacture, sustainability and reason for choice.

o 3D drawings can be easier to understand than 2D as they look more like the real object.

o For GCSE, two types of drawing methods are used: perspective and isometric.

o Sectional drawings show how an object would look if cut through.

o Exploded drawings are 3D drawings which show how a product is assembled.

o Scale maps help people to understand the real dimensions of an area from a drawing. Site plans are the drawings of a site. Schematic drawings are produced for a specific purpose.

o A surface development is the 2D shape which is cut out and folded to make a 3D form.

o Pie charts are used to show proportions within the data; bar charts are used to show comparisons between data; pictographs are similar to bar charts (and also show comparisons) but are easier to understand because they use symbols; line graphs are used to show changes in data.

o Logos can be made of pictures, symbols and words. The corporate identity of an organisation is more than just a logo.

o Symbols, ideograms and pictograms need to be simple and easy to understand.

o Flowcharts are used to explain a process.

o Feedback loops redirect the user to the place where a decision was made.

o Sequential diagrams are used to show a set of instructions graphically so that they are easy to follow.

o Schematic maps use straight lines to simplify routes.

Other useful resources

Developing a well-designed market survey questionnaire will ensure that you get the information you need about your target market.

These surveys can be conducted in writing, in person, via email or over the phone. Read more: How to Create a Market Survey/ www.eHow.com.

chapter 5
Products and applications

Introduction

A product needs to have quality in both design and manufacture. One on its own is not enough. The best designs will stand the test of time, although new technology will date some products more quickly.

5.1 **Quality of design**

For the purposes of this section, the quality of the design has nothing to do with how well it is manufactured. It is all about the fitness for purpose, what we think of aspects such as form, colour, texture, and our responses to the product.

The quality of a design is dependent upon how we see it working for us. As we go through the process of using or interacting with a product, our understanding improves. It is this understanding and experience that fashion our belief about the quality of the design. A good design will appear to be easy on the eye, aesthetically pleasing, and will function properly. Some designs have become classics; the London Underground map is a good example: it does what it is supposed to do in that it communicates the information, but not only that, it works for so many people in such an efficient manner.

The function and appearance of our environment are critical to our wellbeing. The influence which

design has on the environment has never been greater; we find ourselves learning, working and living in situations that, if well designed, enhance the experience.

Activity

Choose a confectionery product or item of food packaging, and explain why you believe it to be a good-quality design. Be sure to consider and explain function, appearance and appeal, as well as how it is suited to everyday living.

Quality of manufacture

How well is it made?

A product can be well manufactured but still be a poor design. Conversely, it can be precisely fitted to work with ease and accuracy and yet not function properly. When a graphic product such as a piece of packaging is well made, the materials will be fit for purpose, the colours will be consistent, the shape precise and the folds exact. All of this is achievable, and yet the design can still be poor.

If you were looking at how well a pop-up book is made, one of the first things to consider would be the material from which it is made. It is always possible to use a range of materials; card, in this instance, is the most suitable. The card, can be cut, hold its shape and be sufficiently durable, as well as being readily available in a range of colours. Most important, it can be finished to allow sticky fingers to be in contact with the book without coming to harm!

Another advantage of choosing card is that the material is frequently used for other purposes. This means that the methods of manufacture, treatment and potential are all well known. There exists a whole set of testing techniques available to ensure accurate quality controls, plus a range of techniques that will allow production in large quantities in a safe environment. Some of these existing techniques can readily be transferred to new materials without loss of accuracy.

Key terms

Classic design – something of lasting worth which has been designed or evolved.

Durable – having a long usable life.

Tolerance – the degree to which something is allowed to differ.

Tolerance

This term refers to the degree to which something is allowed to differ. Recently, banners for a point of sale outside supermarkets have been made from Tylek (a material that acts like a cloth but does not tear) with the image printed on by a digital format, without any loss of quality. Checking the colours on the banner was carried out by matching them to a chart within the tolerance stated.

Working to a tolerance is also important if there is a series of components to be fitted together. Components are frequently bought in from different suppliers and then assembled on a production line. The degree of accuracy must ensure that all of the components readily fit together.

Activity

Collect three different pieces of packaging that show how the tolerances have been checked. The markings are usually to be found on the tabs or hidden parts of the package.

Key point

Quality must be inherent in both design and making. Quality frequently has a personal perspective. One person may believe the quality of a design is good, but has not worried about the potential of the product to be reused or recycled; this property could be essential for someone else. Hence their ideas about whether it is a quality design will differ.

Exam tip

Find examples where the differences between quality in design and manufacture are clear. Be able to write about these differences in clear and concise terms.

5.2 Life cycle of a graphic product

There are four main stages in the life cycle of a graphic product:

○ introduction and evolution
○ growth
○ maturity
○ decline.

The actual life cycle of a product is not really a smooth line as shown in Figure 5.1, but is subject to fluctuations which can be difficult to interpret accurately.

Analysing the product life cycle can help to forecast movement and aid strategies for the manufacturer. Weak points can be identified and targeted for improvement.

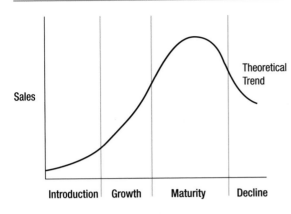

△ **Figure 5.1** A product life cycle graph

Key term

Life cycle – the longevity of a product, from inception to obsolescence.

Introduction and evolution

The **introduction** and **evolution** of a product are often the most challenging time when the concept becomes a reality. The product starts to move from the idea, which is possibly as a solution to a problem, and gradually evolves into a viable proposition. These are not stages which can be recognised separately as the designer and the product will not make progress in a linear fashion. For example, the product will be introduced to the market at a later stage than the evolution of the product itself.

It is a very challenging time and can demand long hours of application without much progress. It is now that some problems are encountered which were not obvious. Perhaps the designer is forced to go back to the start, if he/she encounters legislation of which they were not aware. During this period, patents and trademarks are obtained, prototypes are made, materials sourced, fabrication begins and, most importantly, quality standards are established.

Distribution of the final product is often selective and can look haphazard from the outside.

At this stage, the marketing costs are high and advertising is essential to introduce the product to the market. This is also the time of greatest risk and opportunity. Some products will not make a profit at this stage, and finance can be a problem.

Growth

Growth comes about as a result of rapid sales and an increase in demand. The market share is improving, and the areas of demand are clear and need to be addressed. Maintaining the quality of the product, getting it to the consumer and reaching a wider audience are paramount. It is possible that the product will be 'tweaked' slightly to iron out any teething problems encountered. There will be strong competition from other manufacturers, and this may influence pricing or the support services to the product.

Maturity

As the product gains **maturity**, competition will be greatest. Pricing, emphasising product differences, the distribution network and the range of the audience will be critical to keeping competitors at bay. Continued growth can be dependent on uncontrollable factors such as economic change, technological breakthrough, fashion or social influences and even political swings.

Decline and replacement

Most products have a period of **decline and replacement**. To extend the life of the product, new features are often added and loyal customers targeted for sales. Now is the time to reduce costs on advertising and market support, perhaps even to sell the product line to someone else.

Key point

Always try to give an example when describing products or applications.

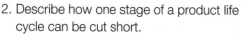

Activity

Select a product that you have used, such as a fountain pen or a magazine, and describe its life cycle. Use a sequence of diagrams to help illustrate your answer.

Exam practice questions

1. State the main stages of a product life cycle.
2. Describe how one stage of a product life cycle can be cut short.

Stretch yourself

Compare and contrast two different products where the life cycles are significantly different. You must explain the differences and why they exist.

5.3 Understanding the needs and wants of customers

We are all consumers in some form or another. As such, we have an insight into consumer demands. Some products are sold as a response to demand, and others as a market push. A market push is where the manufacturer has developed a product that will meet a need or a want. The mobile phone is a good example of this type of product.

Key term

Market push – manufacturer develops a product that will meet a need or a desire.

Factors to consider

To ensure that the manufacturer targets their customer accurately, they have to be aware of the following factors:

Who is the customer?

The customer might be a specific target market, such as youth or older people. If this is the case, the designs will be influenced by specific aspects. There is no point in producing a graphic product for a youth market if it is seen as outdated and not fashionable.

What is the type of product being bought?

If the life expectancy of the product is very limited, such as a card entry badge for a special occasion, then the method of making and the materials used will be critical to the cost and success. If, on the other hand, the product is a piece of packaging for an expensive wrist watch, it will be of more importance than just containing the watch; the packaging will play its part toward the emotional response to the product. The colour, texture and reassurances generated by the form and the delight that can be engendered by the unwrapping and discovery will all combine to create a positive experience for the consumer, and mean that the packaging is likely to be kept as a storage container for other things.

Why is the product bought?

The reason for the purchase will not be the same in every case. The product may be an artefact in its own right, such as a birthday card; or perhaps it is an integral part of a series of products, such as a set of recipe cards that fit together in a display box. The customer may be making the purchase as a fashion statement, or because others have the same item. And, worryingly for the designer, what may be seen as perfectly acceptable in one culture may be totally inappropriate in another.

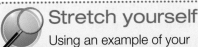
Stretch yourself

Using an example of your own choice, explain how the manufacturing of a product might take longer than the time for which it is used.

How is the product to be used?

Short-term usage requires a different set of criteria from a purchase that is made for long-term use. Reference materials may be used infrequently, but they still need to be attractive and encourage us to return to them whenever the occasion arises. Materials for partially sighted people, or those who are physically less able than others, could potentially be used in a very different way and, consequently, make very different demands of the designer.

What do these factors mean for the designer?

This type of information helps manufacturers to develop new products and recognise trends. Finding out and recording more about the customer and what they buy and when helps manufacturers to understand their spending patterns. This sort of information can also be obtained through market research using face-to-face or telephone interviews, or online surveys.

Although this strategic planning does help the customer to obtain what they want, it can also be used to encourage consumers to spend more money than they might otherwise have done.

Key term

Trend – changes over a period of time.

Activity

Describe two specific ways in which your local supermarket targets you as the customer. Give three reasons why supermarkets issue loyalty cards.

5.4 Judging the quality of a graphic product

In order to be able to judge the quality of a graphic product, you need to have a system, criteria or standard against which it can be compared. Making a comparison against your thoughts will not give the process enough rigour, and over time you are likely to change your opinion.

Factors to consider

A checklist approach can be used for this process, in the same way as factors affecting the needs of customers. The following is a list of six questions that will help to determine how well the graphic product performs.

1. **Does the product meet the initial specification?**

   This is not always easy to determine. You may have to take on the responsibility for the design when the original specification was not yours. The usage can change, and the solution is no longer good enough.

2. **Is it easy to use, or does it appeal to you?**

   It is important to rate or score this aspect to obtain a degree of interest, and a means of comparison. Frequently the outcome of this type of work is illustrated in graph form, which can be used to break up a page of text and convey the information much more clearly.

3. **Does it do what was intended, and do we get enjoyment from the use?**

   We must be sure that the product **meets the need**; it should fulfil expectations.

4. **How well does it suit or fit into its environment?**

   If the product does not blend into its environment, or looks out of place, then it is not **fit for its purpose**. It cannot be classified as a good design.

5. **Has it been made from renewable energy sources and materials?**

   It is essential that the **materials are appropriate for the product**. A good example of this is the egg carton: it is made largely from recycled materials, and is a very strong container offering plenty of protection to the eggs.

6. **How easily can it be disposed of after its usage?**

   We do not want waste packaging to be around for years to come. If the packaging was made from starch, then it would degrade over time. The important point is to determine the **appropriate time frame**, and use this as a selling point of the product.

> ### Key point
> In an examination it is easy to go 'off topic' when writing about this section. Reread the question a couple of times, and make sure that your answer addresses the question. Do this before moving onto the next question.

>
> ### Activity
> Using the checklist above, evaluate the graphic products shown in Figures 5.2 and 5.3.

△ **Figure 5.2** A point of display

△ **Figure 5.3** An MP3 player display

Summary

The reason one product is chosen rather than another is very largely down to personal preference. It can be, for instance, the quality, the technology or simply that it is fashionable. Better decisions are generally made if the product is rated against a series of predetermined criteria. Unfortunately, establishing just what those criteria are is not always easy and can change over time. Political, social or cultural changes are outside the normal references for most designs, yet a change in the tax laws or the dominant culture of the area can influence how designs develop.

The customer and the product have to be matched to enable a need to be satisfied and a supplier to make a profit.

Exam practice questions

1. Choose a leaflet that describes the features of a stately home, a sports facility or an activity. Such leaflets are usually one sheet of A4 folded in three. Judge the quality of the graphic product using the questions listed in the relevant section of this chapter

2. As a result of your findings, make three recommendations for the improvement of the leaflet.

3. Explain the differences between a market push and a customer pull (demand).

4. Describe how a change in the design of a product might be brought about by the users.

5. Give two examples of a product with a limited life expectancy.

6. Explain the difference between the growth and maturity stages of a life cycle using a product of your choice.

Learning objectives

By the end of this chapter you should have developed a knowledge and understanding of:

○ how to improve the product through ongoing and summative evaluation
○ using criteria and end users to enable objective evaluation
○ testing the product
○ testing against the specification.

Introduction

It is unlikely that the product you first produce will be successful in every sense. It is the same as anything we do in life; it can be improved with rehearsal and by paying attention to the detail. Sometimes it is better to leave a product development to a later day and come back to it fresh; you are more likely to see mistakes and potential flaws. However, there has to be a time when you stop the evaluation and make a decision to progress, or you will miss the deadline for the GCSE.

There are a number of ways in which a product can be tested and evaluated. This chapter explores ways in which you can improve your design by carrying out some simple tasks.

6.1 Ongoing evaluation

It is important that you evaluate your ideas and their development, as this will improve your outcome.

○ As a result of the review, add comment, and importantly, sketches which show how the changes you are recommending will influence your outcome.
○ Be specific about the changes you are making: explain yourself to the reader of your project. Reviewing the work is not enough on its own; you must make sure that you **use the information** rather than just collect and collate.

○ It is ideal if you have a client who can help give you an objective opinion. A friend or relative can be good, but beware that they are not just saying what you want to hear, so that they do not upset you!
○ Make valid points, rather than unreal claims.
○ Add to your sketches some detail of the processes, sizes and materials, as this will help to explain the changes you are proposing.
○ Evaluation will also help you to think through your proposals and ensure that the solution offered is as refined as possible. Make some changes that will push the boundaries of your design; you can always reject them at a later stage.

Evaluation techniques

There are a number of techniques you can use, and each of them is explained separately in this chapter.

1. Test the outcome and assess how it meets your initial specification.

2. Look closely at the materials and the techniques used to make the product.

3. Refine your idea with the addition of some of the changes.

4. Use a checklist to see to what degree the priorities you established initially have been met.

5. Create a test to try out your solution beyond the expected limits.

6. Engage others in using your product to see if they find it as easy to use as you do.

6.2 Test the outcome against your initial specification

As you have word processed your specification at the beginning, this process is straightforward. You can simply copy and paste the specification into your work. Each of the specification criteria can then be reviewed and tested in turn. For example, if you had been designing a container to hold 90 fine, wavy savoury biscuits (such as Pringles crisps), then part of your evaluation might read like this:

'The tube can easily hold 90 biscuits, but it is not too big and therefore not wasteful of materials. Because of its size, it is also possible to transport the container in a small rucksack. Interestingly, the biscuits fit neatly onto each other, enabling each of them to gain strength and protection from the one above and below.'

Exam tip

Bland comments such as 'I like this; it is a nice colour,' are totally unacceptable. You must explain your thinking and be sure to state why you have reached your conclusions.

You should then review each aspect of the specification in turn. You might have listed some aspect of the specification as being more important than the rest. If this is the case, then make sure that you deal with these aspects first. It might be that you no longer think part of the specification is relevant. This is not a problem; it is a positive point that will need further explanation. What you have to do in this case is explain to the reader just why that aspect is no longer so important.

Activity

The following list is part of the specification for a box for tissues given to a group of KS4 students:

o The box must be big enough to hold 50 tissues.

o The box must be made from a smooth and glossy card.

o The opening should be perforated and allow easy access to the tissues.

o Most of the legislative details should be on the bottom of the box.

o The colours used should suggest that a clean and sterile product is housed in the box.

Using a box of tissues and the five bullet points above, test and evaluate how well your box meets these criteria.

6.3 Materials and techniques used to make the product

These are the easiest aspects of your work to review and test. You know which materials and techniques you have used, so in your mind substitute them for different materials or techniques. Now go through various aspects of the product, checking the differences. What are the major changes, and how would the outcome be improved?

For example: a magazine or leaflet might be printed in black and white, but if you changed the technique and used colour, every page could be enlivened and the relevant sections shown in the exact colour throughout the leaflet. Photographs could be introduced and the layout of the page altered to make it more interesting. The solution would not have to be formulated to communicate the changes to the client (in this case, the magazine editor); a layout mock-up could be used, similar to the one shown in Figure 6.1. The reviewer of the existing magazine is correct when she says that it could easily be improved.

What is good about the magazine is that it is easy to read, and you can understand what you are reading. It has used a range of colours and has a green border, at the top and bottom of the page. The pages are clearly numbered, making it easier to find your place or a specific topic if needed.

The layout could be clearer. The introduction of a title, in bold writing and underlined if necessary, would help to direct the reader to the important parts.

However, it is also difficult to relate the picture to the writing as they are too far apart. The topics need to be separated. The different topics could be in different colours and then the colours could match the borders of the page. They could be put on a separate page, but this might be expensive and mean that the information was too spread out.

The editor of the magazine is readily able to see the suggestions or changes. Once these have been agreed, the magazine can be reformulated. This is the same for your own designs. Small changes can be made and improvements added to your work. Evaluation does not necessarily mean that you have to start again: small modifications can often have a significant effect.

◼◼ OS NEWS ◼◼

On 2 August 2010, and which we reprint below.

'My father, Klaus Schiller, pioneered and championed the use of endoscopy in gastrointestinal investigations. He was motivated by the highest standards of medical excellence and a commitment to patient care: endoscopy was not envasive like surgery and was more effective diagnostically and therapeutically. He was a man of the enlightenment, literally in the case of his medical speciality, and metaphorically in his abhorrence of ignorance, poverty and inhumanity.

Born in Vienna, Klaus came to England in 1938 after the Anschluss. His parents' families, like many others, were non-practising Viennese Jews; ironically, he had been beaten up in the school playground for being one. Within a few days of his arrival, speaking not a word of English, he was packed off to boarding school. Yet he never remembered learning the language or having an accent, and, in adulthood, was slightly embarrassed to use his childish German.

My father gully embraced England and Englishness. He always agreed with his friend the hepatopathologist Peter Scheuer that 'the best thing that ever happened to us was to come to England'. After attending Clifton College, Bristol, he went on to study medicine at Oxford University. He was appointed senior registrar at the Radcliffe Infirmary, Oxford in 1962 and joined St Peter's Hospital, Chertsy, as consultant physician in 1967. He retired from the NHS is 1992.

Overseas News

From Magnolia Avenue, Manchester, Massachusetts, Michael CAMPBELL (56–57) writes with compliments on the expanded May issue and all of the photos of the 1960s Reunion. 'I was looking for Peter Row', he says, 'and the best that I could do was to spot a white-haired man in a grey jacket wearing a blue shirt and red tie on the two candid shots on the bottom of Page 6 close to the binding and also with his back to the camera on Page 7, mid-way up the page. Was I correct?'

Yes, that's Peter. Well spotted Michael – Ed

'It's been such a long time since I last saw him, so please forgive me if I am wrong. Time changes us all. Going forward with the OS News you will be surprised how that layout with all the pictures will stimulate new interest among the alumni about BSC. The latter part of this month two of my closest classmates from BSC days will visit us here in the Northeast for a couple of weeks. We plan to spend our time telling old stories, fishing on Lake Winnipesaukee and just relaxing.'

OS Veterans' Dinner

Friday, 25 March 2011

For those 65 years old or thereabouts

Partners particularly welcome

Royal Cambridge Hotel

Dinner, B&B £70; Dinner only £25

Additional nights at same rates

Some OS were in the Sixth Form for three years whilst others left after the Fifth, so it is thought that 65 or thereabouts is a better benchmark for qualification.

Peter Collett's letter in the May edition of OS News was a great insight into the atmosphere. Ladies are welcome and many have admitted that they were apprehensive before they came but were given a warm welcome and felt very much at home.

Many OS make a weekend of the event and Cambridge is a good centre for shopping, the arts, the wonderful Botanic Gardens, etc.

△ **Figure 6.1** Outline of text being reviewed

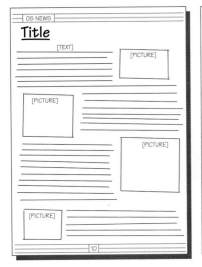  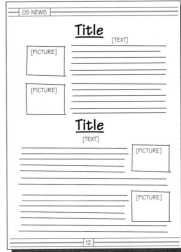

△ **Figure 6.2** Three alternative layout roughs presented

6.4 Refine your idea

Make changes to your product and then check the outcome with the same rigorous tests which you used on your first outcome.

> **Key term**
>
> **Refine** – reduce to its purist or best form.

A board for a game might start by being folded in half, but in your evaluation you decide it would be better folded into four. The evaluation will now not only influence the board, but will also change the size of the box in which it is packaged.

It is good practice to take an everyday product and review, evaluate and propose changes to its design. It may help you to begin the evaluation process, and give you a better understanding of the stages involved.

A GCSE student has completed the following review of two Monopoly sets, and will use the same process when reviewing the game she is making for her GCSE project. She has used two sets of Monopoly to help with a comparison; the first set she believes was designed in the late 1960s or 1970s, and the second in the 1980s. It is interesting to see how the format has changed.

- ○ *The colours represent the estates, and they become more expensive as you go round the board. They are quite vivid and consequently more appealing in the more recent version of the game.*
- ○ *Commodities and stations are priced collectively and the space is not coloured.*
- ○ *The association between the image and the square for supertax is amusing. Those who pay supertax can afford diamond rings!*
- ○ *The size and colour of the money have changed. The money has been improved by being smaller. It would be possible to mix the money if some had been lost.*
- ○ *The packaging has been improved as the game now looks more fun, and yet is not any different.*
- ○ *The early packaging is very wasteful on layout and would therefore cost more.*

She also felt that the deed cards were outdated and has made a suggestion to update them.

BOW STREET	
	£
RENT – SITE ONLY	14
" with 1 house	70
" with 2 houses	200
" with 3 houses	550
" with 4 houses	750
RENT WITH HOTEL	950

If a player owns **all** the sites of any colour group, the rent is **doubled** on **unimproved** sites in that group.

Cost of houses	**£100 each**
Cost of hotels	**£100 plus**
	4 houses
Mortgage value of site	**£90**

TITLE DEED

My design

 Figure 6.3 Deed card changes designed by a GCSE student

Activity

Compare the suggested changes drawn in Figure 6.3 with an original deed card. Design a card that will improve on both of the cards. Remember that you must keep the essential information and make it easy to read and understand.

Another GCSE student chose to redesign the money when reviewing the Monopoly game. He used a computer to carry out the process. Figure 6.4 shows his idea, in the stages of development. To the right of each of the images is the drop-down menu.

△ **Figure 6.4** The stages of redesigning Monopoly money

Activity

Take one of the bank notes in a Monopoly set. Redesign the note in the style of a chosen graphic designer such as Harry Beck or Alberto Alessi, or a graphic artist of your choice.

6.5 **Using a checklist to assist evaluation**

Take this list of questions as the minimum checklist for evaluating whether your initial priorities have been met. Remember to be honest, and always fully explain your thinking. Use full sentences.

1. What is it about the appearance of your solution that makes it such a suitable answer?

2. How well does it work in the way you initially wanted it to work?

3. How do the colours enhance the quality of the product?

4. Why is the material used the best possible in the circumstances?

5. In what way is your product the right size for the intended use?

6. Why does it fit so well with the environment in which it is used?

7. What makes it safe to make or use, regardless of the situation?

8. What was the most difficult element to make? State how you overcame any problems.

To further enhance your work, try using the next set of questions which demand more understanding.

1. Which elements of your product are designed with economies of scale in mind?

2. What did you build into the design to ensure that it was reliable, or at least low maintenance?

3. Explain why you used your choice of finish on the product.

4. Which parts were designed with either **obsolescence** or recycling in mind?

5. How did you cater for the transport and storage of the product?

6. What elements make your design solution significantly better than those already available for sale?

7. How were you able to make it in the available time?

8. Why is your product intuitive to use and consequently better for the user?

 Key terms

Priorities – determining the important aspects or factors and placing them in order.

Obsolescence – a product that is no longer wanted. This can be brought about by an upgrade in technology, or improvements in performance, or because the product can be no longer used or is antiquated. It does not have to be antique: computers created in the 1990s are now largely obsolete.

A GCSE student used the checklist technique to evaluate a page in the pop-up book shown in Figure 6.5.

△ **Figure 6.5** A page from the pop-up book *Haunted House* by Jan Pienkowski (Walker Books)

Interestingly, some items of the checklist could not be used (for example points 2 and 8 of the first list), as he did not make the book himself. The evaluation points are not too elaborate, and reflect his feelings and perception of the book. Not all of the points that he made are listed here. Look at how often he suggests an improvement or modification.

1. *What is it about the appearance of your solution that makes it such a suitable answer?*

It has lots of pop-out shapes and pull-out flaps. This makes the book interactive and exciting, and this is good because the book has been designed for young children. To improve the amount of information on each page, there could be a rotation wheel that puts different images under the flap; this gives a greater variety of image on the page and could also change the story.

2. *How do the colours used enhance the quality of the product?*

The colours are very bright and exciting. The book needs to keep children interested all the time and if the colours were dull, the book would not be interesting. As the book will be read more than once, there need to be areas of interest that can be reread and the colours can be described.

To improve the design further, some of the colours could have been made more vivid, which would make them stand out better, especially if they were more important to the story.

3. *Why is the material used the best possible in the circumstances?*

The book is made out of card. This is the best choice, because it is cheap to get hold of, easy to print on and the processes are well tried. It is also easy to fold and will not fold wrongly or crease because it has fold memory. To make the book more interesting for the child, they could have used some different textures on the book because young children like to interact with the book.

4. *In what ways is your product the right size for its intended use?*

It is a big book. This makes it easier to read because you can have larger fonts. Also, because the book is big, it means that the pop-outs and flaps are easier to use and more exciting. To improve the pages, they could have been made even bigger so that they could have even more pull-outs and flaps on a single page.

5. *Why does it fit in so well with the environment in which it is used?*

It is designed for a young child's environment. The book does not have much writing to read, but there are lots of pictures, which is good because not all young children can read easily. To improve the amount which the children learn from the book, there could be more similarities to the child's environment, so that the parents could refer to them.

6. *What makes it safe to make or use, regardless of the situation?*

The pages are thick; this means that the child will not cut themselves on the paper.

They are easy to handle and the pop-up will not cause problems. The colours are fixed and will not run or smudge. To increase the product life, the book could have a set of instructions for the levers; this would prevent damage to the book so that it can be used again and again.

6.6 **Test your solution beyond the expected limits**

You need to create a test to test your solution beyond the expected boundaries or limits. For example, when creating a promotional freebie that holds a product such as handcream, make it smaller or larger than you had intended, or fill it with more cream than anticipated and review the results of a series of tests. Look for results beyond the obvious; it might burst, but could a slight change in shape enable a better performance?

Key term

Shifting the boundary – moving the limits that are established.

Key points

- Not all products will be capable of the same review.
- Sometimes a non-interaction (the question you are asking as part of the evaluation which appears to have no relevance) can be just as important to the evaluation.
- Testing and evaluating need to be carried out systematically.

6.7 **Engage others in using your product**

This is sometimes known as a **user trip**.

If you have created a game using a pack of special cards, let others play with them and then observe carefully how they are used and how easy it is to use your creation.

○ Be careful to observe closely and do not accept any point as the right way.

○ Decide if you can use this information to improve your game by incorporating some of the ideas.

○ Record the opinions of your users and use this to influence the changes you make.

○ Use quotes from the users to bring this section alive.

On occasions the outcomes are not always as you might predict. Simply because the end users do not use your product in the way in which it was intended does not mean that they are wrong, or indeed that your product is a failure. What you want the end user to bring to this situation is an unbiased and objective perspective. If there is lots of laughter when your game of cards is being played, it could a major success!

Key term

User trip – employing others to evaluate the product through their interactions.

6.8 Modifications and summative evaluation

Having evaluated your design, you should have a series of modifications either completed or ready to be done and then tested.

For the evaluative statements to be successful in your project folder, it is essential that you analyse the product methodically. Missing stages are likely to create a shortfall in the information you refine, and could be important to the development of your product.

The summative statement on pages 91 and 92 is a short version of the kind of statement which you will need to make for your project. Using the information gleaned from the procedures

Activity

Before you begin this process, carry out the simple routine below:

Select the six factors which are the most important aspects of your design. For example, if you were creating the menu for a Chinese takeaway restaurant, it would be essential for the following items to be considered:

1. type of paper

2. layout of the page

3. font

4. name of the restaurant and the telephone number

5. listing of the food

6. cost of the food.

In selecting the six most important aspects, you will quickly see whether you have covered the major elements of the evaluation. Make sure that you have explained why your six aspects are critical to the success of the product.

set out in this chapter, it is possible to create three action-packed A3 pages of evaluation and potential modifications.

Summary

○ Every product can be improved through the evaluation process.

○ Modifications must be made for any improvement to be recognised.

Activities

1. Using five items from your specification, analyse any page from this book.

2. (a) Collect together three sketches of your ideas, from any one of the tasks you have undertaken for this course. Show these ideas to five of your class friends and ask them to rate their favourite in order of preference.

   (b) Get them to write down a comment about each of the designs.

   (c) From this information and your own opinion, determine which the most popular design is. State clearly why you think this design has been selected.

3. Review, evaluate and propose changes to the design of a gift card from iTunes or a similar gift card.

chapter 7

Social, cultural, moral, environmental, economic and sustainability issues

Learning objectives

By the end of this chapter you should have developed a knowledge and understanding of:

- how moral, social and cultural issues should be considered in design
- the terms 'ergonomics' and 'anthropometrics'
- the use of ergonomics and anthropometrics when designing
- why labelling is important and a requirement on packaging
- why sustainability is a key area in design
- how recycling is not the only eco-friendly solution
- the six Rs of reducing waste.

Introduction

In this chapter we will explore the influences placed upon a designer by the changing world and society around us. As cultures mix, moral boundaries, local laws and traditions are questioned and tested globally. Resources that once were considered would last forever are running out; pollution and waste are beginning to affect our everyday lives.

We design for humans on a daily basis; we match designs to physical size and current environment. Why would we want to consider designing and planning for the longer term? With labelling we can make informed choices at the point of purchase that can match our own moral code, or inform us on the impact of the product on the environment, our health and quality standards.

7.1 Moral and social issues

It is the responsibility of the designer to consider the moral, social and cultural aspects of their design. It is the responsibility of the consumer to justify and feel comfortable with their choice when purchasing a product. How would you feel about buying an item which has used underpaid child labour in its manufacture? Would you pay £20 more for a pair of trainers if they were guaranteed to have been made by adults who were given a fair pay and a living wage?

Moral and ethical issues

There are several issues which may cause a **moral** problem in products, such as:

- the use of child labour
- animal testing to develop cosmetic and pharmaceutical products
- genetically modified crops in food
- products that encourage deforestation
- global transportation of day-to-day items
- the use of heavy pollutants in a product's manufacture.

It is important that companies who have a strong moral ethos indicate this in the packaging. A positive reaffirming message could support the buyer's choice. Ethical trading is a growing concern as we source materials and labour from around the world. A company would be considered to be ethically trading if it ensured safe working standards and procedures in its factories, set out fair pay and working conditions for its employees, and considered the impact of production on the local environment. Greater detail can be found on the ethical trading website www.Ethicaltrade.org.

Fairtrade

Consumers can be assured that they are not buying goods produced by an exploited labour force if the packaging carries the Fairtrade Mark. The Fairtrade Foundation uses a set of international standards which the producer must adhere to in order to be recognised with the symbol for trading in the UK.

◁ **Figure 7.1** The FAIRTRADE Mark: for more information visit www.fairtrade.org.uk

> **Activity**
> Can you list five points for and five against the use of genetically modified food? What would convince the general public that using these crops is safe?

Cultural issues

These days products and advertising exist in a global market. When developing a product, a strategy should be produced to ensure that it is not offensive to different cultures, ethnic minorities or countries to which the product is being exported. This **cultural** consideration can be crucial to the success of the product. Recently, the HSBC bank ran a series of television advertisements, identifying how cultural variations can affect business at a local level.

In the global market, a product can be seen all around the world. The product need not necessarily be sold in a country or a particular region; the internet can provide access to images of packaging and advertising from around the planet. Bearing this in mind, it is essential for a designer to be aware that images can be found offensive across cultures, race and religions. Investigation is needed to ensure that a name or graphic will not be misinterpreted and offend.

Social issues

A valuable skill for a designer is to know how to anticipate trends and look at the **social** implications of the products they design. UK society has changed greatly over the past decades; being aware of the changes and the current social issues is important to a designer. For example:

o the ageing population
o obesity
o smoking and alcohol use.

The fast-food chain McDonald's likes to promote the social, family atmosphere of their restaurants and the healthiness of their meals. A few decades ago, their advertising campaign was focused around a clown called Ronald McDonald. Under social pressure this was dropped by McDonald's as it was considered to be promoting unhealthy eating options to children.

7.2 Ergonomics
What is ergonomics?

Ergonomics is the scientific study of how equipment and systems can best match human abilities and characteristics. It considers the **human** usage of design, focusing on the objects which people use, their environment, and their activities.

Designers try to design for the average person when thinking about producing thousands of items of a product. The average person does not exist, but designers can however design for the **best fit**: the thing that suits most people.

Technology is continually advancing; it is of increasing importance that the relationship between people, their technology and their environment is considered.

Activity

Look at the website www. ergonomics4schools.com. Produce a poster highlighting what you consider to be the most important areas covered on this site.

A good starting point when considering ergonomic study is to consider the following:

○ the physical size of the user group
○ the five senses employed when using a product: touch, hearing, sight, taste and smell.

The **interface** with the product is vital. For example, designing an alarm clock would require the following consideration:

○ An alarm clock could have raised buttons so they can be found in the dark.
○ The alarm volume could vary so that the user is gently woken up.
○ The dial could glow enough to be visual in the dark, without lighting up the room.

Taste and smell would be irrelevant in this instance but would be vitally important for a food container, to ensure a neutral smell and no contamination of the food's taste.

When ergonomics is considered in the design of a product, the product is easy to use and feels comfortable both physically and psychologically.

△ **Figure 7.2** Moulded handles on kitchen utensils offer a level of comfort to the user. The ridge before the blade on knives prevents fingers from straying onto the sharp blade.

The product is easier to use when ergonomics has been applied in its design. Ergonomics helps to support the safety and the comfort of the product when in use.

Anthropometrics

The physical size of people is one aspect of ergonomics. This part of ergonomics is called **anthropometrics**: the gathering of data to find common patterns in people's size. When anthropometrics is used, ergonomics has been applied in the design of a product.

Anthropometric data is often presented in the form of charts. For example, they could give common sizes on many aspects of the human form which are useful to designers, such as:

○ the best sitting height
○ average spans of hands
○ eye level
○ working surface heights.

The human physique is important, but human ability should also be taken into account: strength, posture and the range and frequency of movement.

Activity

Print out a series of five letters and numbers. Each line can be progressively smaller, similar to an optician's chart. Place this on a wall at an end of a corridor. Walk towards this poster; for each line, measure the distance from the chart when the characters become clear.

This information is important when designing signage or a poster. From this you can calculate at what distance from the sign the writing becomes legible.

Data can be taken for static application (standing still) or for dynamic application (a person in motion).

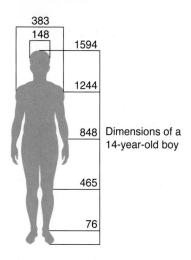

383
148
1594
1244
848 | Dimensions of a 14-year-old boy
465
76

△ **Figure 7.3** The data of the human body is placed on different charts. These can be for hands, head or the whole body

Using anthropometric data

Anthropometric data is often applied using percentiles. The data is gathered from a huge range of people and plotted onto a graph which shows the frequency, or the number of people with a given size. The most common size is called the 50th percentile. The people with the very largest and the very smallest sizes are not as common as the 'average person'. The top five per cent and the bottom five per cent of the population are highlighted on the chart.

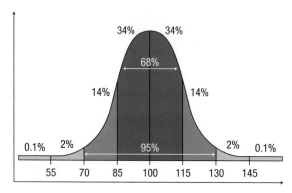

△ **Figure 7.4** The percentile chart is used to plot data results. The first and last five per cent are ignored in the figures

These are called the fifth percentile and the 95th percentile. People who are extremely large or very small are rare, and will fall into the fifth or 95th percentile on the chart.

It is unusual to include these small percentiles in the calculations when designing for the mass population. When using percentiles, it is possible to accommodate 90 per cent of the population within your design considerations. One person in ten will fall outside this.

Points to consider in your design

○ What is the user group range?
○ Can it be adjustable?
○ Is it designed for the best-fit average?

The charts and data used can vary on the user group of the product. The anthropometric data will vary with age, sex, ethnicity and disability.

Considering ergonomics in design

If we look at a handheld power tool, we can find how ergonomics (the human factor) could be applied to its design.

1. The weight of the drill is important; construction workers may use the product for long periods of the day. The weight argument could also be applied to the domestic DIY user; the time of use could be shorter, but the user could also be physically weaker, such as an older person.

2. The angle of the handle attached to the body of the drill will dictate how we hold the product. Is the same arrangement acceptable when up a ladder, or drilling through a floor? What effect would a second handle on the product have on how the user would hold the product?

3. Are the grips smooth? How will this be affected by perspiration on the hands? What size is the handle? Will a rest or support be required?

4. Will heat from the motor be dissipated near the hand? Is the power on/off switch accessible when the product is being held in the operating position? Have you considered left-handed operators?

△ **Figure 7.5** Consider the ergonomic factors in a handheld drill

 ## Activity

Design brief for party glasses:

1. Design and make a card prototype of a pair of fun party glasses. The glasses could follow a theme, such as beach party, sports party, make-over party. Think about the design that can sit on top of the frames.

2. Using anthropometric data, work out the best fit size for your class. Remember to take the fifth and 95th percentile out of your calculations.

3. Measure the key point shown in Figure 7.6; carefully measure your colleagues and place your data in a table like the one below.

4. Can you now calculate the mean key dimensions of your glasses?

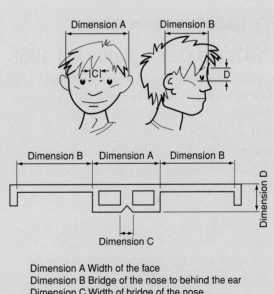

Dimension A Width of the face
Dimension B Bridge of the nose to behind the ear
Dimension C Width of bridge of the nose
Dimension D Cheek bone to eyebrow

△ **Figure 7.6**

Name	A	B	C	D
Average				

Key terms

Anthropometrics – the dimensions and physical shape of a human.

Ergonomics – the design of a system or product that takes into account the human body and senses.

5th and 95th percentiles – the very extremes of a surveyed population. These are generally not included.

Static dimensions – dimensions used when not in motion.

Dynamic dimension – the dimensions used when a person's motion needs to be considered, for example the best height for a stair tread.

7.3 Understanding labels

The Trade Descriptions Act 1968

In 1968 the government passed the **Trade Descriptions Act** which protects the consumer from false or misleading statements on a product. It also covers services and goods.

An offence has been committed if a description is false or misleading, and has a significant impact on the purchaser's ability to use the goods or service as reasonably expected.

A description could be verbal, in writing, or by illustration. Producers need to take care that the photographs on the packaging or tag lines on adverts are not misleading.

The wholesaler is also committing an offence if they sell goods which have had a false or misleading description applied.

Activity

List ten well-known advertising slogans. Discuss if these could be considered misleading.

Product labelling

Product labelling falls under the Trade Descriptions Act. Labels must include information to ensure that the product can be used correctly and safely. For example:

○ indoor heaters and fires will carry warning labels to ensure that they are not covered when used to dry clothes

○ children's toys give advice on the suggested age of children playing with the toy.

Food

Food products fall under the Food Labelling Regulations 1996. The ingredients of the food product must be shown by weight. Labelling on food (such as sweets) must show whether it contains types of additives, such as antioxidants, sweeteners, colours, flavourings, flavour enhancers and preservatives.

△ **Figure 7.7** Food labelling is controlled by legislation

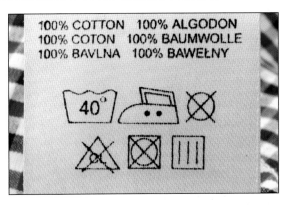

△ **Figure 7.8** Care labels are used on clothing so that damage through washing is limited

Barcodes are not compulsory. (Barcodes are a series of vertical lines which are optically read. This digital code relates to the supermarket information on the product, pricing, stock control, etc.) However, because of the way that supermarkets operate, every product usually carries a barcode on its packaging.

Films

The British Board of Film Classification symbol seen at the cinema and on DVDs indicates the age groups that would be suitable to watch the film. This classification is a visual indication, in line with the Trade Descriptions Act. It indicates what content and themes will be seen by the viewer, matching the purchaser's ability to use the goods or services as reasonably expected.

Clothes

Clothing contains labels which indicate the care that should be taken during the laundry process, from washing temperatures to ironing recommendations. These ideograms are the same ones used on detergent packs, irons and washing machines. The regularity of the symbol makes the process of using the product and caring for it easier.

Health warnings

Health warnings are required by law on some products. Alcohol and tobacco are good examples of these. Pharmaceutical products will always list possible side effects and under which circumstances the drugs should not be taken (for example, 'may cause drowsiness', 'not to be taken with alcohol', etc.).

An age warning can indicate to parents that a product is not suitable for children. It could be that the product has small parts that can cause a choking hazard.

Consumer confidence

Labels are an important source for consumer confidence when purchasing a product. Some companies have their own label for quality or luxury; for example, Tesco has its Finest range. These products are produced using a higher grade of ingredients and this is highlighted in the packaging.

This claim of quality, however, is made by the company producing the goods. The British Standards Institute (BSI) is an independent test that companies can apply for. A product or service that conforms to a British Standard will show the BSI number to confirm that it has been made to recognised standards.

Knowledge link

For more information on British Standards, see Chapter 9.

Products like safety equipment and children's toys **must** conform to British Standards to be allowed to be sold in the UK. The products are sent from the manufacturing company to be independently tested by the BSI. If the product passes the Standards test, it will be awarded a Kitemark; the company can then pay for this to be displayed for the customer.

The CE mark is a statement by the manufacturer that their product meets the EU directives. This is not an externally tested standard; it is the responsibility of the company to ensure that the directives are met.

Knowledge link

For more information on European standards, see Chapter 9.

7.4 **Sustainability and judgements**

During the course of producing a design, a designer will make judgements and compromises. The final design could become a balance of cost and materials used. The balance will become more complicated to calculate, as extra considerations are needed for ergonomics, materials, manufacturing processes, environmental issues, aesthetics, branding and social implications.

Environmental issues are becoming more important as a consideration in the design process. It is important that we see the product as a whole, and think about the extraction of the raw materials, the energy used in the manufacturing process, and the implication of the use and disposal of the product.

△ **Figure 7.9** Mining for resources is a huge industry

△ **Figure 7.10** Transportation adds a huge environmental and financial cost to the product

Life cycle of a product

Products made out of raw minerals may go through the following process: having been covered for millions of years, the raw material is dug out of the ground in one part of the world, reshipped at great expense to Asia, extracted, manipulated and formed into an object using a great deal of energy, shipped to Europe, used for a few days, then taken to a landfill to be buried underground for thousands of years.

A life cycle analysis is used to calculate the true cost of a product. Costs are noted of the energy and non-renewable resources being used in the extraction and processing of the raw material, through the time expenditure of the development, and then disposal (which could be the energy and effort used to recycle the product into a usable state).

When the true ecological cost of a product has been calculated, it can be designed to minimise its total **environmental footprint**. It is one thing to design an item with recyclable materials; it is another to consider how this recycling will take place. **Eco design** takes into account the whole life cycle of the product. Eco-designed products can now be given an eco design label, to help the buyer make an informed choice about the goods they are buying. Product labelling of plastic types is a way of helping this end process.

Built-in obsolescence

A product can be designed to have a certain life span, or **built-in obsolescence**; after a certain date, the product will stop being useful or will look outdated. From a commercial point of view this is successful, as new and replacement items will need to be bought. However, from an ecological standpoint this puts more of a strain on our natural resources.

This obsolescence can occur in several ways.

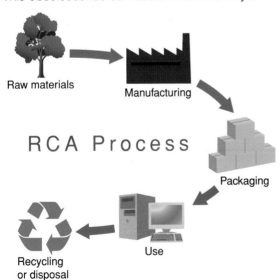

Raw materials

Manufacturing

RCA Process

Packaging

Use

Recycling or disposal

△ **Figure 7.11** A life cycle analysis shows the whole environmental cost of a product

◁ **Figure 7.12**
EU Ecolabel

Knowledge link
For more information on built-in obsolescence, see Chapter 4.

Systematic obsolescence

The system around the product changes, making the product redundant. A good example is in the computer gaming market; in purchasing an Xbox Kinect™, old games will become out-of-date as consumers will want to play using the new interface.

Activity
Collect images of the history of the mobile phone to produce a time line. On each phone, list the functions that can be found; for example, does it have a 1 megapixel camera? Draw points on the time line where you would be persuaded to upgrade to the next model. Give reasons why.

As technology advances, old gadgets become obsolete. Think of touch screen and smart phones, compared with a mobile phone from five years ago.

Component obsolescence

A product may become obsolete because a component runs out. For example, it is easier to buy a new inkjet cartridge or pen than attempt to refill them (unlike petrol in a car).

△ **Figure 7.13** Inkjet cartridges are often disposed of when empty

The six Rs of waste

Consumers and manufacturers are encouraged to think about environmental costs. Waste reduction is often thought about in six categories, each beginning with the letter 'R'. Commonly they are referred to as the six Rs:

○ reduce
○ recycle
○ reuse
○ refuse
○ rethink
○ repair.

Activity

List and illustrate items you throw away after use. Next to each of them, make a note of their dimensions, the cost, and how long they last in use. How many of these items do you use in a year? Imagine these are laid out end-to-end; how far would this waste stretch?

Reduce

Manufacturers design for fewer materials to be used, less energy to be used in manufacture, and for more economical packaging and transport.

Many goods are made in the Far East; these are brought into the UK in container ships. Transport costs are calculated by the cubic metre. By flat-packing and packing intelligently, the manufacturer can save space in the container; they can then ship more for the same money without adding to the fuel cost of the ship.

Recycle

Raw material is recovered from the parts of the product. Metals, plastics, glass and card can be processed to be reused again. Recycling is not the greenest option, as energy and resources are used in converting the item back into a workable form.

△ **Figure 7.14** The recycling symbol is commonly used

Reuse

The reuse of a product is a positive way to stop waste. Reusing carrier bags in supermarkets is now actively encouraged. Less common now, daily milk delivery and collection a brilliant reuse of the glass milk bottle.

△ **Figure 7.15** The reuse of this bathtub ensures that the farmer has drinking water for his livestock

Refuse

The consumer can refuse to buy the product because of his or her judgement and beliefs. They might consider that the product is over-packaged, or that it is inefficient to run. This places a strong emphasis on companies and designers to deliver what the customer wants.

> **Activity**
> Look at fridges and refrigerators online or in an electrical shop. How is it indicated how efficient to run they are? Which are the best, and what does this mean?

Rethink

Consumers and designers can rethink the use and need for products. Do you need to replace the whole mobile phone, or could a new screen or skin be added? Can the same job be done in another way? If a rigid foam is being used as a filler during transportation, could this be replaced with a biodegradable paperfoam?

> **Activity**
> Redesign the packaging for an Easter egg. Highlight how all of the six Rs have been considered in your design. In a product life analysis, state which process would have the least harmful effect on the environment.

Repair

Can the product be repaired? Often it is easier, cheaper and more convenient to replace a product that is broken, or partially not working, than it is to repair. Within the design of the product, could replacing parts or refilling be a prime function and selling point of the item?

Packaging is possibly the worst graphic product in terms of producing waste. Posters and point-of-sale items have a built-in obsolescence when selling a product on a limited or special offer.

> **Activity**
> During the Second World War, a government public information slogan was to 'make do and mend'. This was to encourage people to repair or put up with items that were worn, as raw materials were scarce. Find out whether the UK was a greener (more environmentally friendly) nation 70–100 years ago. This can be presented as a better/worse chart.
>
> Design a new 'make do and mend' poster that would relate to today's society.

△ **Figure 7.16** The 'make do and mend' posters from the Second World War were a reminder that many materials and goods were in short supply

Summary

This chapter has shown that we need to consider how we look after the world's resources and how, through the global market, products used in one country can influence and have an impact on people living on the other side of the world. Common labelling of products helps us make informed decisions about where and how a product has been manufactured, the care we need when using the product, and the safe and appropriate disposal of the product after use.

Exam practice questions

1. (a) Give an example of a product that has obsolescence built into it.

 (b) When purchasing an inkjet printer, as well as the cost of the machine, what other costs might you need to consider?

 (c) Why would a manufacturer build a degree of obsolescence into a product?

2. (a) In today's world of diminishing resources sustainable product design is very important. Consider the design of a new product and describe three important factors that support eco design.

 (b) Describe two problems that are associated with landfill.

 (c) How are plastics identified and sorted for recycling?

3. (a) What anthropometric data would be useful when designing:

 (i) a chair?

 (ii) a telephone?

 (iii) a pair of reading glasses?

 (b) Designers consider ergonomics during the design process. Why does this ultimately benefit the consumer?

 (c) A percentage of a specific user group is excluded when designers look at the anthropometrics and ergonomics of a product. Give the reasons why.

4. (a) Discuss why the British Standards Kitemark would give a consumer confidence in the product they are buying.

 (b) List three things that you consider to be basic rights in the workplace.

5. (a) Sustainable product design reduces the impact the product will have on the environment in the long term. Identify a product and suggest how its impact on the environment could be reduced throughout its life cycle.

 (b) Design a full-sized net for an opening box 10 cm × 5 cm × 2 cm.

 (c) If five of these were to be made, how could waste material be reduced?

Learning objectives

By the end of this chapter you should have developed a knowledge and understanding of:

o the component parts of a CAD/CAM system
o different CAD/CAM and ICT input and output devices and their function
o selecting appropriate CAD, ICT and graphic software
o benefits and costs of CAD/CAM and ICT
o how to produce virtual reality models using CAD software
o how the electronic transfer of data permits designing and manufacturing activities to take place in different geographic locations
o using photographic evidence to record any stages during design, manufacture and promotion.

Introduction

ICT is an essential tool for designers. Useful ICT applications include software that allows them to amend designs quickly and easily, manufacturing machines linked to this software, and the ability to communicate ideas, concepts and finished designs to clients and suppliers.

8.1 Identify the component parts of a CAD/CAM system

A graphic designer using Information and Communications Technology (ICT) should understand that a **Computer-Aided Design (CAD)** and a **Computer-Aided Manufacturing (CAM)** system comprises two main components: hardware and software.

o The **hardware** components include any item that you can physically touch, place on a desk or move from one room to another, such as the screen, mouse or keyboard or manufacturing equipment.
o **Software** is the set of instructions (or computer programs) that tell the computer or manufacturing machine what to do. In industry as in schools, computers are usually

connected via a central network server, where all the information is stored and exchanged. Networks may be hardwired for security or they may be connected through wireless access points.

If the server is the hub of the hardware system, the operating system is the special software which allows the two components to work together. The operating system (Windows®, Linux or Apple®) tells the computer how to use all the software programs to control the different devices it can be connected to, such as the plotter, scanner, printer, etc. These hardware devices attached to the system are usually described as peripherals.

What is a CAD/CAM system?

A CAD system uses computer technology to aid in the design of a part or product, especially the drafting (technical drawing and engineering drawing). CAD is a method of changing hand-drawn sketches of initial ideas into neat, scale drawings that show the exact dimensions and proportions of how a product will be seen when it is manufactured. Designers can use CAD to draw and test their ideas on the screen. Designs can be saved to the computer at any time for editing and changing, which is less time-consuming than using paper and redrawing completely to correct mistakes or make changes.

A CAD/CAM system links the CAD software to a CAM machine that can understand the design and make a real-life version of it.

Key terms

2D – drawing in two dimensions.

3D – drawing in three dimensions.

CAD – Computer-Aided Design.

CAM – Computer-Aided Manufacture.

The simple orthographic drawing shown in Figure 8.1 was produced on a 2D vector-based package. A Computer-Aided Manufacturing (CAM) machine, such as a vinyl or laser cutter, could be used to cut out the lettering for modelling the finished package.

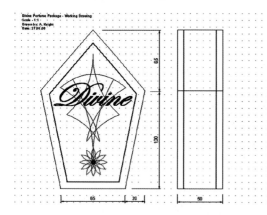

△ **Figure 8.1** A simple 2D drawing

Exam tip

Use CAD to demonstrate creativity, and to develop and communicate ideas.

Key point

CAD should be used to develop and refine your designs.

Activity

Investigate the cost of the equipment and software needed to build a CAD system.

8.2 The function of CAD/CAM and ICT input and output devices

As we have seen, a CAD system uses computers in the design of a part or product. A CAM system uses computer-controlled machine tools to manufacture products drawn using CAD programs.

CAD input devices

A CAD input device is any device that allows data to be entered into a computer system. For example, a scanner is used by the designer to transfer images into the computer from a 2D drawing or picture. There are many other input devices, but the main ones used are the mouse, digital cameras, keyboards and graphics tablets. Digital cameras and graphics tablets are used in the following ways:

1. A digital camera stores digital images and videos, which can be downloaded onto a computer hard drive. Once the images (or video footage) have been downloaded onto a computer, the user can save or modify them. These images would normally be saved either on a flash drive or the school computer network.

2. A graphics tablet is a flat, digitised pad on which a special pen creates images that can be copied or pasted into the computer.

CAM output devices

A printer is one of the many output devices attached to the computer, and creates a 2D product that can be shaped into 3D packaging. CAM creates real-life versions of components designed using CAD. Although CAM and **Computer Numerically Controlled (CNC)** equipment has its roots in the industrial revolution with the invention of the Jacquard loom, its first proper use was for car body design and manufacture in the early 1970s. Now simple CAD equipment is available to most designers.

◁ **Figure 8.2** Jacquard loom – the first programmable device

 Key term

Computer Numerically Controlled (CNC) – machines which are controlled by a number system.

Vinyl cutter

Vinyl cutters are commonly found in schools and design studios; this is one of the more basic CAM machines. They are used to cut adhesive vinyl, and work in a similar way to a plotter. Vinyl cutters are available in a variety of different sizes, from A4 upwards. They are commonly used to create designs or logos to stick on to packaging, or lettering and images for vehicles.

The Roland CAMM1 and Stika are examples of vinyl cutters.

△ **Figure 8.3** Vinyl cutters

Engravers

Engravers can produce anything, from lettering through to quite intricate graphics on a variety of different materials such as soft metals, wood, MDF and plastics. The Roland CAMM 2 and Vision Phoenix 1212 are examples of engravers.

Engravers are commonly used to create nameplates, logos, directional signs, machine components, promotional goods, raised lettering, PCB pattern engraving, etc.

△ **Figure 8.4** Engravers

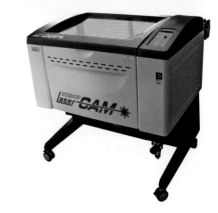

△ **Figure 8.6** A laser cutter

△ **Figure 8.5** Examples of work using engravers

△ **Figure 8.7** Work produced using a laser cutter

Rapid prototyping

To fabricate 3D objects, a rapid prototyper is used. This is like a printer that works in three dimensions: information on how to construct the product is sent from the CAD drawing to the rapid prototyper in the form of a code (Stereo lithography file or STL format).

Production of the object depends on the type of technology used by the 3D machine. Usually the process binds one layer at a time (laser on resin or adhesive on powder) and then it can slowly build the product up using layers. Similar to a printer, some machines can add colour. This technology is sometimes referred to as 3D printing.

After finishing, the end result is a representation made quickly in a solid material that can be evaluated and tested.

Laser cutters

Laser cutters are now more common in schools. Laser cutting works by using a high-power laser beam controlled by computer to cut flat sheet material such as card, MDF and acrylic. Depending on the type of material being cut, the material melts, burns, vaporises or is blown away by a jet of air.

One of the advantages of laser cutting over mechanical cutting is the high-precision cutting it allows, and also the lack of physical contact between the cutting edge and the material. One of its disadvantages is the high energy required.

Always check that the correct material is used for the machine – harmful vapours must be filtered and made safe.

△ **Figure 8.8** Rapid prototyping

CAD/CAM equipment is a tool in the same way as a craft knife, cutting mat or any other tool – they all have their place in designing and production. CAD/CAM should be used in conjunction with traditional hand skills to enhance work and demonstrate a range of different creative products.

Key points

CAD/CAM is an ideal way to produce items in quantity.

CAD/CAM should be used as a tool.

CNC machines can be used to shape Styrofoam™ graphic products.

CNC machines can be used to make vacuum-forming moulds.

 ## Key terms

Engraver – CAM machine for cutting and engraving MDF/acrylic and soft metals.

Laser cutter – CAM machine for high-precision cutting of almost any material.

Vinyl cutter – CAM machine for cutting and scoring vinyl, paper, card, etc.

CNC – Computer Numerical Control.

MDF – medium-density fibreboard.

Exam tips

o Use CAD/CAM to improve your design work and making work.

o Use CAD/CAM with traditional skills.

o Use CNC as a tool to enhance the making of your product.

8.3 Select and use appropriate CAD software

On the market there are many different and competing CAD software packages available, which all work in basically the same way but appeal to different markets. The CAD software packages commonly used in schools range from 2D vector-based drafting systems such as Techsoft 2D design to more complex and sophisticated 3D solid and surface modelling software such as the market leaders ProDesktop and AutoCAD Solidworks.

CAD can be used in two dimensions (2D) and three dimensions (3D) depending on the capability of the programs used by the designers. 2D drawings are used to create working drawings similar to those created by pencil and paper on a drawing board. Working drawings can show views of a product from many different angles. 3D CAD allows you to create an image of a finished product and then render the idea with colour and shading on the screen and view the product in the environment for which it was designed.

On most packages it is part of the design that the CAD package should be relatively simple to learn the main commands and functions to produce drawings. Most software will have online or inbuilt tutorials that give the operator the basics. There are many specialist textbooks or guides available on individual CAD packages. Free software is often available to students to encourage them to use – the software companies regard this as promoting their software to the designers of 'tomorrow'.

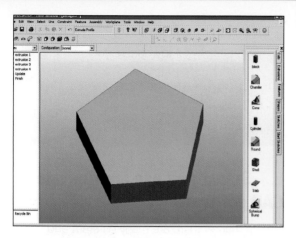

△ **Figure 8.9** 3D drawing

Graphic designers use whichever CAD package they have available to develop their designs and demonstrate their ability to present work using a range of graphical techniques, and clearly communicate details of the chosen product designed.

Exam tip

Demonstrate your skills when you produce an accurate drawing of one of your designs.

Key term

2D vector drawings – can be scalable to any size without any loss in the quality. It makes them ideal for objects that have to be resized frequently, such as company logos.

Key point

CAD can be used to produce a drawing that can be updated and changed as your designs improve.

8.4 **Appropriate ICT and graphic software**

Applications are almost always separate programs from the computer's operating system (OS). Lots of applications put together as a package are sometimes referred to as an application suite; for example, Microsoft Office puts together a word processor, a spreadsheet and several other applications. Applications software is often designed and manufactured for use with a specific platform or operating system; for example, in Microsoft Office for Windows 7, Microsoft Office is the application but it is designed specifically for Windows 7 (the platform, or OS).

Different types of software
Text software

Text software refers to programs specifically designed to process text, called **word processors**. A word processor is a computer application used for the writing, producing, editing, formatting and printing of any sort of text. Word processors include functions such as grammar and spellchecking programs, and a wide range of style options. Microsoft Word is the most widely used computer word-processing system.

Database software

A computer database is a structured collection of records or data which is stored in a computer system. Database software stores and organises a set of specific data, and is known as a **database management system (DBMS)**.

Databases can carry out complex searches for different information and provide answers in a fraction of the time it would take to do it manually. For example, a school database could search or filter the data for all girls in Year 8 who travel to school by car. This is a complex filter:

1. Girls
2. Year 8
3. Travel by car.

The resulting list of names could then be sorted, alphabetically by forename or surname. A variety of different sorting methods (such as alphabetically, numerically) are available within database software.

Search results can be printed out in list form or put into pre-formed documents. The results from the above search could be mail-merged with a letter home, so that the names and addresses of all the girls' parents would be put on to the letters and printed out automatically.

Key terms

Applications software – programs designed for specific tasks.

Applications suite – a collection of programs (such as Microsoft Office).

DBMS – database management system.

Spreadsheet software

A spreadsheet is a computer application which simulates a paper worksheet. It is in the form of a grid consisting of rows and columns. Each square of the grid is called a cell, into which you can input alphanumeric text or numeric values.

Spreadsheets can contain formulas: each cell can be calculated from the contents of any other cell (or combination of cells) on the same or different spreadsheets. If one of these cells is changed, the calculations change accordingly.

Spreadsheets are often used for financial information because of their ability to manage and respond to a large range of data changes.

Graphics software

Graphic software includes functions such as creation tools, editing tools, filters and automated rendering modes. There are many different types of graphic software, designed and used for specific applications.

Graphic design software

Desktop publishing (DTP) software is used in graphic design for general image editing and page layouts. It is used by newspapers and magazines to design the layouts and set the output ready for print production.

Multimedia development software

Multimedia development applications are graphic software packages with audio, motion and interactivity, such as software for computer simulations, creating and editing electronic presentations (slide presentations), and games.

Image development software

Images can be created from scratch with most art software. Specialised software applications are used for more accurate visual effects. These visual effects include those listed below.

○ **Photo editing:** designed for rendering with digital painting effects and hand-rendering styles that do not appear computer-generated (such as Photoshop).

○ **Photorealistic effects:** creating the illusion of a photographed image using 3D modelling and ray tracing features to make images appear photographed.

○ **Digital painting:** used for digital painting, representing real brush and canvas textures or handicraft textures such as mosaic or stained glass (such as Photo-Paint, Corel Painter).

○ **Vector editors:** ideal for the solid, crisp lines seen in line art and poster-type effects.

Key point

Text, graphics and database software can be used for different tasks and functions.

Exam tip

Try to use appropriate text, graphics or database software whenever appropriate.

8.5 **Benefits and costs of CAD/CAM and ICT**

CAD and CAM

CAD is the process of producing designs using a computer. The purpose of CAD is to visualise the designer's ideas on screen; once these images have been finalised, a series of informative drawings can be produced.

The main advantages of CAD are:

○ **Higher productivity** – standard orthographic drawing can be produced almost immediately after design completed.
○ **Reduced design time** – shortcuts are available and work can be completed quickly when you are familiar with its features.
○ **Less time required for modifications** – drawings can be seen on the screen, and mistakes and modifications can be seen in 3D or magnified using zoom features.
○ **Ability to repeat designs** – designs can be altered without erasing and redrawing. It is easy to include variations.
○ **More accurate designs** – standard components can be combined to make new designs quickly. Presentation drawings can be lifelike in quality.

The main disadvantages of CAD are:

○ **Cost** – expensive to purchase the software and hardware.
○ **Training** – if the operator is not familiar with the CAD system, it is difficult to use.
○ **Technology** – if there is a computer problem, all data will be lost.

The advantages of CAD far outweigh the disadvantages. The cost-for-benefit analysis would show that CAD nor only reduces the product development expenses and time, but it also increases the accuracy of drawing and encourages error-free design. Because of these reasons, the graphical design sector has bought into CAD technology.

CAM allows the manufacture of the product designed in CAD, using computer-controlled technology.

The main advantages of CAM are:

○ **Accuracy** – product components are made to a specification and to numbers required.
○ **Flexibility** – modern CAD production allows the quick interchange of tooling so that a range of products can be programmed into the machine.
○ **Stamina** – manufacturing is non-stop; the machines never get tired or need a break.
○ **Maintenance** – faults can be predicted and the machine only stopped for routine servicing.

The main disadvantages of CAM are:

○ **Breakdown** – specialist engineers and expensive parts may be required to repair the machines.
○ **Poor design** – an inaccurate or poor design will produce a poor product. Rubbish in equals rubbish out.
○ **Waste** – if the CAD system runs without checking mistakes, the machines can produce large amounts of costly scrap.

Exam practice question

What are the advantages and disadvantages of using CAD and CAM?

CNC

The term CNC describes machines which are controlled by a number system. Early models of similar machines had controlled leather parchment with holes punched in by hand; these were replaced by paper tape, and now CNC machines are driven by computer code. The machine codes directly tell the machine heads how to move and where to cut so that a product is created.

The main advantages of CNC are:

○ **Sustainable** – machines can be used continuously and only need to be switched off for occasional maintenance.

○ **Repeatable** – machines are programmed and each manufactured product will be exactly the same.

○ **Upgradeable** – machines can be upgraded by improving the software.

○ **Manageable** – one person can supervise many CNC machines.

The main disadvantages of CNC are:

○ **Cost** – CNC machines are more expensive, although costs are coming down.

○ **Deskilling workforce** – CNC machine operator only needs basic training, and many of the old manufacturing skills are lost.

CNC machines are improving in design and capability at a rapid rate. The cost of installation is reduced because of the investment in the machines, and the workforce is now training to be reskilled to meet the demands of using and maintaining the complex CNC machinery. The disadvantages of the technology are less significant than the advantages.

In graphics the main use of CNC machines is to form and shape Styrofoam™ or expanded polystyrene as part of a graphic product, or to shape MDF, Jelutong or balsa wood to create moulds for vacuum forming using HIPS.

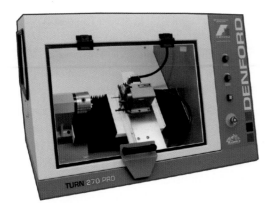

△ **Figure 8.10** A Denford CNC lathe

Key terms

Styrofoam™ – polystyrene thermal insulation, blue or pink in colour and denser than expanded polystyrene.

Expanded polystyrene – polystyrene foam, typically white and made of expanded polystyrene beads.

HIPS – high-impact polystyrene sheet.

Jelutong – a low-density, straight-grained hardwood, similar to balsa wood.

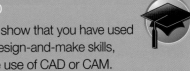

Exam tip

You need to show that you have used a range of design-and-make skills, including the use of CAD or CAM.

8.6 Virtual reality models using CAD software

Virtual reality (VR) is defined as a realistic simulation of an object or environment, including three-dimensional graphics, by a computer system using interactive software and hardware. The object can be created by the designer on screen, and then placed to give the viewer an illusion that the product or the environment is real.

The evolution of the virtual reality model has followed game technology. Early games were blocky and unreal, but gaming technology has now evolved to highly believable images in high definition and 3D.

Interior designers can design stage sets, using libraries of ready-made objects (furniture, figures, lighting, wall covering, etc.) to populate their world. The client is allowed a virtual 'walk through' to test the design and make changes before the real construction work starts.

An aircraft engineer could design a landing system for a modern jet fighter and test the performance in a simulated environment. The simulation can test different materials, alter the properties and stress the system until it fails, and all in virtual reality. The pilots can use games technology to fly the fighter jets in a virtual world of the flight simulator.

△ **Figure 8.11** Flight simulator

Perfume packaging can be designed using CAD. When the information is ready to be presented, the product can be placed in a simulated shop environment by cutting and pasting the file on the screen. The virtual reality will allow us to 'walk around' the point of sale, admire how the product is shown off to its full potential and evaluate how we can improve the product before manufacture.

△ **Figure 8.12** Perfume packaging in a virtual environment

Most CAD software packages have built-in tools to construct an object and test the design in environment. ProDesktop, Solid Works and Google SketchUp™ enable the graphic designer to create their ideas and place them in a virtual world.

Key terms

VR – virtual reality.

Walk-through – placing the viewer in the virtual environment.

8.7 **Electronic transfer of data**

Electronic transfer of data permits designing and manufacturing activities to take place in different geographic locations. Data can be stored and then distributed in many different ways. The modern mobile phone is used as a memory device which can have instant worldwide distribution.

Data storage

Data storage involves the recording and storing of information. Electronic data storage is storage which requires electrical power to store and retrieve the data. On a computer, data is stored on the hard drive, which stores quickly accessible graphic media and holds large files. Graphical products are memory-hungry.

Data can be stored either in digital or analogue form; this information is called electronically encoded data. The advantages of storing data electronically are it that is easier to search, update and revise, and also more cost-effective than alternative paper-intensive methods. Digital data is easy to store, with a variety of storage devices available on the market.

The disadvantages of storing data electronically are that electronic storage media are, like paper, prone to decay, and also can be affected by mechanical defects over a long period of time. This disadvantage can be overcome by backing up the information to other hard drives or other devices that hold electronic data.

Information processors such as computers or iPads also have built-in dynamic memory storage, as well as the ability to access the removable recording devices to retrieve and store information. Removable recording media use a device that holds and stores digital information (such as DVD, pen drives, memory cards).

> ## Key terms
>
> **Permanent component** – a computer hard drive.
>
> **Removable recording device** – DVD, CD-ROM, pen drive, memory card.

Data sharing

Computer systems can store or share information on a small, local scale or on a worldwide scale. Information about a product or design can be shared in many different digital ways – by email to a small group of chosen recipients, or on a website accessible by everyone throughout the internet. Once the information is on the internet, it can then be accessed throughout the world in seconds by all the information search engines, such as Google or Yahoo.

Sharing information requires consideration of different levels of access. Who is allowed to see that data? Companies and organisations may have information which they wish to share with all or some of their employees, but not with competing businesses on the internet.

One way to safeguard the distribution of

information is to use a **Local Area Network** (LAN), which acts in the same way as the internet, and only gives access to the data to other computers on the network. The LAN managers have total control of what information can be accessed. School systems have a LAN environment where information can be securely stored, access to information can be allowed and potentially dangerous information can be filtered and blocked (such as a virus).

Information on a LAN can be managed so that only designated people who need access to the data can retrieve it (for example, financial data or databases containing employee information).

△ **Figure 8.13** Computer network

The Data Protection Act

Product design information can be protected, but in order to protect individuals from having confidential and personal information shared between organisations without their permission, the UK Parliament passed the Data Protection

△ **Figure 8.14** Storage devices

Act (DPA) in 1998. This Act creates rights for those who have their data stored, and responsibilities for those who store or collect personal data.

Under the Data Protection Act, individuals have the right in law to view the data held on them by an organisation, and to correct that information if it is inaccurate. The holders of the information are required to ensure that data is neither used in a way that causes damage or distress, nor for direct marketing.

Exam tip

Always save and back up your work!

8.8 **Photographic evidence in design, manufacture and promotion**

The design process is about identifying, researching, analysing, developing and finally evaluating ideas and images with technology that is available. Designers use photographic evidence from any source, including digital or video, to record stages of design, manufacture and promotion.

△ **Figure 8.15** Digital cameras

Digital cameras

Designers use digital and video cameras as tools for inspiration. Images are captured which they then manipulate and use as the basis for a design. Alternatively, graphic designers can transfer their images directly onto a product using specialist printer inks. For those who dislike drawing, this can be an effective tool to communicate ideas.

A digital camera stores digital images and videos, which can be downloaded onto a computer hard drive. Once the images or video footage have been downloaded onto a computer, the user can save or modify them.

The camera encourages designers to become more open-minded about being creative and experimental. The ability to produce good-quality images easily by taking a photo or video, manipulating and printing it, putting it in a presentation or burning it to a DVD is a distinct advantage. This process is quick and involves lots of hands-on work using photo manipulation software or a video editing suite.

Designers can make a record of a piece of work or a demonstration of a technique, and use this as a tool for comparison later on in a project. Using a camera, the still or moving image can help to facilitate discussion or perhaps just demonstrate the results of the design process.

The cameras retain digital examples of the progress of work, both practical and written, and can also create displays to inspire the design team. Still or video demonstrations can be placed on the internet to test consumer opinion and to carry out market research on a product.

Exam tip

Digital cameras can be used to record the development of practical work.

Key term

Digital camera – a camera which stores digital images and videos.

Summary

Computer-Aided Design (CAD) is the use of computer technology to design and develop ideas.

Computer-Aided Manufacturing (CAM) is the use of computer technology to produce products.

The advantages of using CAD and CAM outweigh the disadvantages.

Virtual reality is a three-dimensional visual world created by a computer.

Digital photographs and video can be used as evidence of manufacture.

Other useful resources

See www.technologystudent.com for information on different design and technology processes and concepts. For computer numerical control, see the following page:
http://www.technologystudent.com/cam/camex.htm

Learning objectives

By the end of this chapter you should have developed a knowledge and understanding of:

○ information regarding the safe handling of tools, materials, components and equipment
○ hazards, risk assessment and how to control the risks to the designer and others
○ legislation intended to protect the public
○ symbols and signs relating to quality assurance endorsed by recognised authorities
○ information used to assess the immediate and cumulative risks
○ how to manage your environment to ensure your own health and safety and that of others.

Introduction

Designers must know about relevant health and safety guidelines and laws, and how to minimise any risk of injury to themselves or others when working. They also need to know how their products should conform to national and international laws and how products are labelled when they meet these standards.

9.1 Safe handling of tools, materials, components and equipment

Graphic designers and manufacturers have a legal responsibility for the safety of their products. The designer has a duty to the users to design a product that is safe and fit for the purpose for which it will be used.

In order to work safely, a designer should have all the necessary information regarding the safe handling of tools, materials, components and equipment. The Health and Safety at Work Act 1974 (HASAWA) is an excellent law which is a good starting point for all safety laws in England and Wales. The Act is very long but its message is simple – the employer has a duty of care for the employee's safety, and the employee has a duty to work safely.

Employers have a duty to make sure, as far as is reasonable and practical, that employees (and visitors) are safe at their place of work. Safety for employees means that training and supervision must be provided when handling tools, materials, components and equipment.

Advice for employers and employees can be provided by the **Health and Safety Executive (HSE)** who cover a varied range of activities, from shaping and reviewing regulations, producing research and statistics, to enforcing the law.

Health and safety information should be displayed in the working environment for designers and manufacturers:

○ Clearly marked instructions for safe use of tools and equipment.
○ Dangers from components and materials should be identified and precautions listed to prevent misuse.
○ Notices should give clear indications of possible hazards in the working environment.
○ The working environment should have adequate lighting and temperature to enable the work to be carried out safely.
○ Adequate training should be given for use of all tools, equipment, materials and processes. A record of health and safety training should be kept and updated when needed.

Key terms

Notices – information displayed in a public place.

Duty – what you have to do.

Good health and safety are supported by a clearly marked working environment which considers the work of the designer:

○ Workplaces should be organised so that processes may be carried out in a safe manner.

○ There should be clearly marked work areas for production, vehicle access, pedestrians, etc.

○ Components and materials should have designated areas. Care should be taken when storing hazardous substances and correct records should be kept to control the dangers.

○ Evacuation exits should be signposted in the event of fire or other serious occurrences. Fire extinguishers and STOP buttons must be clearly marked.

○ It is good practice for risk assessment to be displayed near to hazardous equipment, processes, materials and tools.

Key point

The employer has a duty of care for your safety, and you have a duty to work safely.

Exam tip

Exam questions may ask you to comment on what information you need to ensure that you work in a healthy and safe environment.

Exam practice question

Consider what information you would need if a new piece of equipment is introduced to the manufacturing environment. Whom would you consult?

9.2 **Recognising and controlling hazards and risks**

Almost every part of a designer's job can risk the designer's health or wellbeing; a simple craft knife blade can put us in danger of cutting ourselves. A process, material, substance or equipment that could cause harm or damage is described as a hazard. **Risk assessment** is the process of identifying the hazards that could arise and the risk of someone being hurt by them, so that steps can be taken to eliminate or reduce that risk.

Key terms

Hazard – a situation that can cause harm.

Risk – the likelihood of the hazard occurring.

Activity

Identify the hazards when using a craft knife to cut card. Write down a risk assessment for the activity.

Risk assessment

The Health and Safety Executive produces a leaflet, 'Five steps to risk assessment'. This explains that risk assessment is nothing more than a careful examination of what could cause harm to people in your working environment, so that you can weigh up whether you have taken enough precautions or should do more to prevent harm. You are legally required to assess the risks in your workplace.

The five steps to risk assessment are as follows:

1. **Look** for the hazards: walk around your workplace, check equipment instructions, ask the people you work with what they think.

2. **Decide** who might be harmed and how. Consider all people that may come into contact with the risk and hazards, including visitors and members of the public.

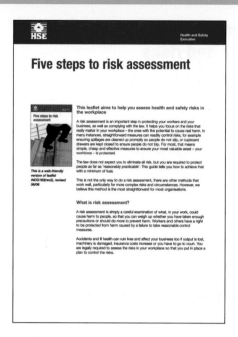

△ **Figure 9.1** The HSE gives detailed information on risk assessment

3. **Evaluate** the risks and decide whether the existing precautions are adequate or whether more should be done. Ask if the risk can be eliminated – do you have to use that chemical or that machine? If you cannot get rid of the risk, consider how you can reduce it. If you are cutting card to make a model, use a sharp craft knife and a safety ruler on a suitable cutting mat.

4. **Record** your findings. If you work with fewer than five employees there is no need for your supervisor to write down the risk; above that number, the employer must record those findings and tell you about any risks and hazards. Precautions must be reasonable and keep the remaining risk low.

5. **Review** your assessment and revise it if necessary. In the design industry there can be a rapid change in tools and equipment; it is important that the risk assessments are regularly updated and changed when needed.

COSHH

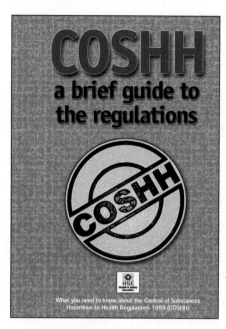

△ **Figure 9.2** COSHH assists the safety of the design industry

Designers often use chemicals and materials in the design and manufacture of products. Using chemicals and other harmful substances may put us at risk. Control of Substances Hazardous to Health (COSHH) Regulations 2002 are the law which requires employers to control substances hazardous to health. Good employers can reduce the risk with hazardous substances by making a COSHH assessment:

○ **Walk around your work area: where is there a chance for exposure to substances that might be hazardous to health?** Include processes that give out fume, dust, vapour or gas, and bring you into contact with liquids, dusts and pastes.

○ **In what way are the substances harmful to health?** Safety data sheets can be found online or supplied with materials and substances. Further advice can be found by contacting the HSE or looking on their website.

○ **What jobs or tasks lead to exposure to harm?** Note these down. For these jobs, how likely is any harm to health? What control measures do you already use?

○ **Are there any areas of concern reported? Check the Accident Book.** All workplaces should keep an accident book for reporting accidents. Examples include burns from splashes, nausea or light headedness from solvents, etc.

If you identify chemicals or substances hazardous to health, you should go through the risk assessment procedures to eliminate or reduce risk to yourself and others.

> **Key point**
>
> Eliminate risk if possible; if not possible, put in place actions to reduce the risk.

Exam tip

Exam questions will ask you to construct a risk assessment for an activity carried out by a graphic designer using materials, tools or equipment that may cause harm.

9.3 Legal information intended to protect the public

In order to protect the public, legislation exists stating what information should be supplied on packaging. This information should include the following:

○ the **name** of the company that made the product – this should be clearly printed
○ the **contents** of the product
○ the **bar code** – displayed for stock control and pricing purposes
○ the safe **disposal** of the container or packaging, with instructions on recycling
○ **health and safety** information about the use of the product.

> **Key point**
>
> The designer must by law include information on the packaging to protect the public.

Special regulations are applied to the packaging of food under EU and UK law. Packaging containing food must include the following information:

○ **name** and **description** of the food
○ list of **ingredients**
○ **weight** or **amount** contained in the package
○ **nutritional** information
○ **preparation** instructions
○ **storage** instructions
○ **name** and **address** of manufacturer
○ **country** of origin.

Exam tip

Exam questions may ask you to comment on what information you need to include on packaging. Consider the additional information needed on food packaging.

Activity

Find out what information should be included on a toy's packaging to protect the user.

Key term

Public protection – the designer/manufacturer has a duty of care to protect the user.

9.4 Symbols and signs relating to quality assurance

Quality assurance is to make sure that the product does what it is designed for in safety. Many companies have internal quality checks along the production process. If these checks meet international and national standards, they can be accredited by the recognised authorities' quality marks. The main recognised authorities are:

○ International Organization for Standardization
○ British Standards Institution
○ CE (Conformité Européene).

Knowledge link
For more information on how you might consider quality in your own work see Chapter 5, Products and applications.

International Organization for Standardization

The name of this organisation, abbreviated to ISO, derives from the Greek *isos*, meaning 'equal'. It is the world's largest developer and publisher of more than 18,000 International Standards.

ISO is a network of the national standards institutes of 163 countries (one member per country), with a Central Secretariat in Geneva, Switzerland, which coordinates the system. Manufacturers display the ISO award on the packaging as a quality assurance of international testing for safety.

British Standards Institution (BSI)

This organisation works with manufacturers, consumer groups and designers, testing standards for products. If the product passes the independently administered test, it can then display the British Standards Kitemark. The Kitemark gives the consumer the assurance of quality that the product is tested as safe and reliable.

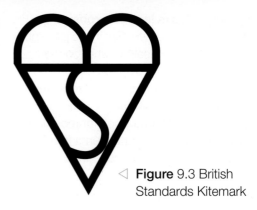

◁ **Figure** 9.3 British Standards Kitemark

CE

The **CE** mark is an acronym of the French term *Conformité Européene*, and is a statement by the manufacturer that the product meets all the relevant legislation in the European Directives. A product bearing the CE mark will have easier access into the European market. A wide range of products (such as toys and household appliances) must meet the CE standard before they can be sold in the European community.

△ **Figure 9.4** The CE mark

9.5 Use information to assess immediate and cumulative risks

Regulations require employers to provide information in the form of specific safety signs whenever there is a risk. The immediate risk in the workplace can be shown using well-designed signs warning of immediate danger such as corrosive materials or flammable materials. Information to assess long-term risk or cumulative risk (such as risks from excessive noise or dust) can be indicated by signs telling the employee to wear ear defenders or dust mask.

The information in the form of signs and symbols must be clear and easy to understand. To attract attention, bold colours, geometrical shapes and strong images are used to convey the signs' messages. The designs specified in the Regulations are already covered by the existing British Standard BS 5378:Parts 1 and 3:1980 *Safety signs and colours*. The Health and Safety (Safety Signs and Signals) Regulations 1996 bring into force the European Union Directive to encourage the standardisation of safety signs throughout Europe; whenever and wherever they are seen, the signs have the same meaning.

Activity

Design a warning sign for the local zoo. The sign must inform the user that they must not feed the animals.

Key term

Geometric shapes – these are used to indicate what sort of information is displayed: for example, warning triangles, instruction circles.

9.6 Manage the health and safety of the environment

In the working environment, all those who are involved in designing and making products have a responsibility for minimising the risk of harm to themselves or to others.

Health and safety considerations of different processes

We should act to ensure the health and safety of ourselves and others in the different ways in which we work.

Designing and making a product

During this process, we should ask the following:

○ Could any of the substances or **materials** used cause harm to the maker or to others?
○ Can the paints or varnishes used to finish the product cause harm to the maker or to others?
○ Can any of the **making** cause harm to the maker or to others?

Wash your hands

Wear eye protection

Wear ear protection

HIGHLY FLAMMABLE

Corrosive

Toxic

Chemicals

△ **Figure 9.5** Immediate danger signs and cumulative risk signs

Finished product

When the product is finished, we should ask the following questions:

○ Are the materials suitable for the purpose, and safe for users?
○ Will the product be strong enough to support any load involved?
○ Have all hazards been sufficiently guarded: moving parts, electrical insulation, etc?
○ Will there be any adverse effects on users: harmful, toxic, etc?

Disposing of the product

When the time comes to dispose of the product, we should ask:

○ Will the recycling of materials cause the release of harmful substances?
○ Is it harmful to dismantle the product?

If the answers to any of these questions lead you think that harm may be caused in your environment, some parts of the product should be redesigned to eliminate or reduce the risk to your safety and others.

△ **Figure 9.6** PPE can help with your protection

> ### Key point
> Designers must reduce or eliminate the risk of doing harm. If safety equipment is provided, it must be used.

If the risk cannot be eliminated, then **Personal Protective Equipment (PPE)** should be worn:

○ To protect the eyes, goggles or face shields can be worn.
○ If noise is a problem, ear defenders will protect hearing.
○ Hands can be protected from substances, materials, tools and equipment by wearing the appropriate protection to reduce the risk of the hazard.
○ Dust mask, overalls and heavy boots may be needed by designers when visiting the manufacturing and where the danger level is increased.

Exam tip
Exam questions may ask what you can do to improve safety if you cannot eliminate the risk of equipment doing harm.

Exam practice question

A machine used for cutting packaging to size produces a fine dust and is very noisy. What steps can you suggest to reduce the risk to the operators?

Key term
PPE – Personal Protective Equipment, to be used when the risk of harm cannot be eliminated.

Summary

Designers may work with materials and in places that may damage health or cause injury. You can minimise these risks to yourself and others by recognising hazards and undertaking risk assessments. The products you design must also meet minimum standards which are identified by a series of labels endorsed by national and international bodies.

Other useful resources

The following websites are useful for this area of the course:

Health and safety Executive Website – free downloadable publications:
http://www.hse.gov.uk

British Standards Institute:
http://www.bsigroup.co.uk

ISO International Organization for Standardization:
http://www.iso.org

Introduction

Systems and control procedures for graphics products require a set of components arranged to carry out a particular function. All systems have inputs, processes and outputs; some will have feedback.

Graphic design systems used in production require detailed planning which needs to be carefully controlled. System controls can be visual, electrical, mechanical or electronic devices. Systems and control production systems must be reviewed for quality – part of a process called quality assurance and quality control.

10.1 Input, process, output and feedback in the production system

A system is a set of components arranged to carry out a particular function. Systems may include mechanical, electrical or electronic components. The block diagram in Figure 10.1 represents a system for producing a batch of leaflets.

- **Input** is what goes into a system: the raw materials.

- **Process** is the change needed to bring about the output.
- **Output** is what comes out of the system: the finished product.

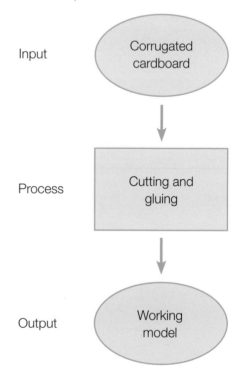

△ **Figure 10.1** Process diagram of a graphic system

128

Feedback

Feedback is a way of changing the input or process as a result of what happens at the output. In a shower system, feedback is a human response to the output from the water taps; if the water is too hot, the user will reduce the heat by turning up the cold. Figure 10.2 gives a feedback diagram of a shower.

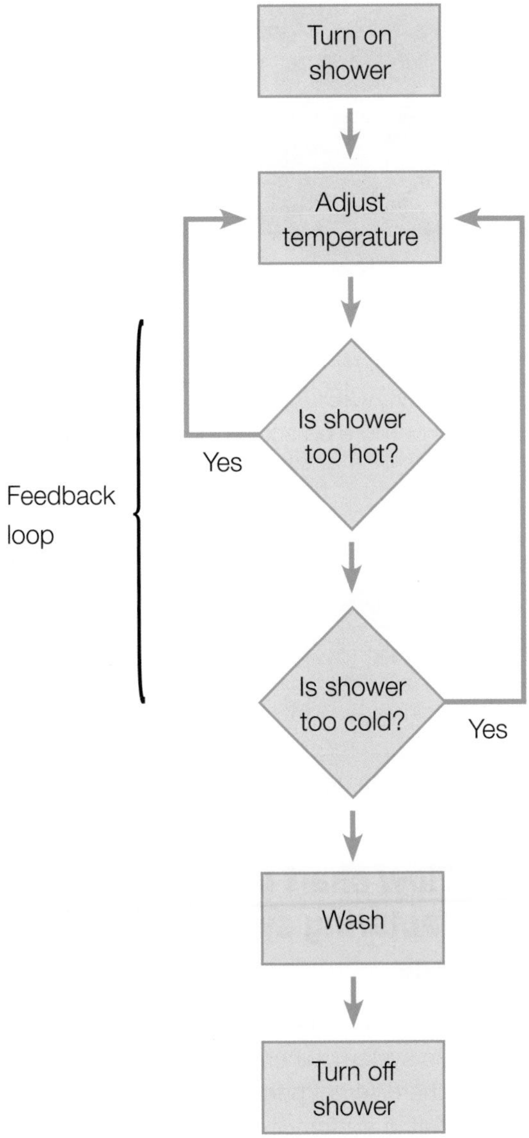

△ **Figure 10.2** Feedback diagram of a shower

Feedback in a production system means checking that the product meets the specification, and adjusting the process to make sure that it will produce the correct output. Some production systems have an **automatic feedback**, when one part of the system switches another part of the system off or on. When this occurs in production system, it is called a **closed system**.

10.2 Logical order of work changes as the scale of production increases

A logical order of work is needed for all manufacturing production systems. It is likely to include the following processes:

1. **Storage** of raw materials, bought-in components, sub-assemblies and part-finished products.

2. **Inspection** of bought-in parts or components to ensure that they are of the required quality; inspection of part-finished artwork or products to ensure that they meet design specifications. Inspection has to be done at all of the crucial points in the production process.

3. **Operation** is the processes of manufacturing.

4. **Movement** of raw materials, part-finished products and complete products.

Scale of production

The amount made of the product will determine the type of production level used. The greater the number of a product made, the cheaper the unit cost per item. **Economy of scale** is the term used to describe the principle that the more items you produce, the cheaper they become to produce.

It is quite rare to manufacture only one of an item ('**one-off**' production) as the cost is often so high, due to the high cost of skilled labour and the development cost. Exclusive point-of-sale display may be manufactured by highly skilled craft workers and designers, but the cost would mean that only one item would be produced.

Most of the designs you see are made in a **batch production**, where more than one item is made. Batch production involves a manufacturer making the same item only for a few days or a few months. A school textbook is a good example of a batch-produced item, with the printer taking about one week to produce many thousands of copies.

When the demand for the product is predicted as high, it is likely that the item can be **mass produced**. This may mean that many thousands or millions are made, and the manufacturer is likely to be making the same item over a long period of time.

Continuous production is when the demand for a product is so high that the item can be made 24 hours a day and seven days a week. Continuous production is used to make items such as cartons for the drinks industry. The carton may be standard and used by a number of drinks brands. The only difference will be the final colours, logo and information which differentiate the various companies. The printed cartons are then sent back to the product manufacturer where they are filled with the drinks and sealed.

> ### Key point
> Know why the method of production of a single item is different to the production of lots of items.

The **just-in-time** method of production is another method of reducing costs. It is designed as a specific method of controlling stock: a company only buys in enough materials to cover its immediate needs for that day. Stock is controlled so that the exact amount of materials arrives at exactly the right time on the production line. Less stock stored in warehouses means that companies may save money.

The advantages of JIT for the companies include:

1. reduced storage costs
2. production run can be more easily changed
3. reduced overstocking of product.

△ **Figure 10.3** Production line

>
> ### Knowledge link
> For more on scale of production and production systems, see Chapter 11.

> ### Exam tip
> You are likely to be asked which production process would be suitable for different products. The examiner will be looking for evidence that you are aware that the one-off model you produce is unlikely to be made the same way industrially.

10.3 Flow chart of a manufacturing system, showing feedback

System flowcharts are used when planning a production system, where you need to work out how the different parts or elements of the manufacturing system fit together to show an order to the process. Each step should fit within the system and be portrayed in the right order of operations. A flow chart is a good way of demonstrating the design process for CD production. The quality control checks are built into the process and show feedback in the system. When the quality check shows a defect, the item is rejected and the production line informed so that changes can be made to improve the processing; the output can therefore be of the specified quality.

FLOW PROCESS CHARTS

Subject: *CD production*

Chart begins: *pre-mastering*

Chart ends: *packaging after final inspection*

Symbols	Description
	pre-mastering – check content
	mastering
	electroplating
	pressing
	metallisation
	varnishing
	label printing
	inspection
	packaging

△ **Figure 10.4** Process flow in CD manufacture (with feedback)

Quality assurance and quality control

For the graphic designer, it is important that the terms **quality assurance (QA)** and **quality control (QC)** are not confused. Quality assurance refers to a standard of quality, whereas quality control is the means of meeting those standards.

Quality assurance is built into the planning for production. The designer must make informed decisions during the design process, ensuring

that the product will be made to the appropriate standard. Standards are produced for designers to work to, with the aim of designing products which give value for money and are economical, efficiently produced and safe for the consumer.

Quality control refers to the measures which the designer can put into place to check that the quality standards specified by the consumer are met by the finished product. The making will be checked at a number of 'critical points' throughout the manufacture. The end product will be finally checked against an example known as the 'norm'.

Knowledge link

For more information on quality, see Chapter 5 and Chapter 11.

Key terms

Quality assurance (QA) – the process through which the designer actually states what quality he or she wants the product to have when it is finally made.

Quality control (QC) – the measures that are put into place to ensure that the quality standards are met at critical points of the making process.

Production line – a set of machinery required to make a product from start to finish.

Key points

Understand the terms quality assurance and quality control.

You will need to apply quality assurance and quality control to a range of production methods.

10.4 Quality control marks and symbols used in the printing industry

At the start of production, the machines used (tooling) will be set to make the exact size. As production continues, there will be slight tooling wear or tooling movement. When quality sampling is carried out, as long as the finished sizes are within the tolerances then production continues. An example of a quality control tolerance is that the size of a drinks carton can have a tolerance of 0.5 mm. This means that the card can be 0.5 mm bigger or smaller than the 'norm'. If the size of the sample falls outside the tolerance then production is stopped. Machine tools are then adjusted when a quality sample is at the end of the tolerance range. This prevents waste product and saves money on materials.

Quality control marks

Registration marks

These are cross-haired lines that help visually ensure that a set of films or printing plates are in line or in register to produce a sharp registered result. Many modern printing presses have sensors which can automatically detect registration marks and ensure the alignment of the machine tools.

Colour bars

Colour bars are a pattern of varying colours that enable visual and numeric quality control comparisons to be made across multiple printed sheets or pages. These help the printer to check that the colour of the inks has remained

the same, and that there is no change in colour from the start to the finish of the print run. The colours are checked with a manual or electronic **densitometer**.

Crop marks

These are crossed lines placed at the corners of an image or a page to indicate where to trim it. Crop marks may be drawn on manually or automatically applied with some desktop publishing software programs. They are also known as **trim** marks. Trimming can then be completed by a guillotine or a die press.

△ **Figure 10.5** Registration marks, colour bar and crop marks

> ### Key term
> **Tolerance** – acceptable range of accuracy.

10.5 The principles of simple mechanisms and relevant components and features

A mechanism creates movement within a product. There will be occasions when the graphic designer needs to include a mechanism in a product, whether it be a board game or a moving sign.

There are four types of movement

1. **Rotating** – turning in a circular motion.

△ **Figure 10.6** Rotating movement arrow

2. **Linear** – moving in one direction.

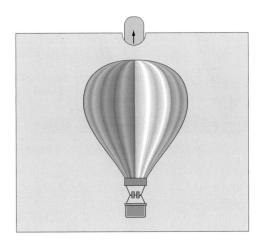

△ **Figure 10.7** Linear movement

3. **Reciprocal** – moving backward and forward.

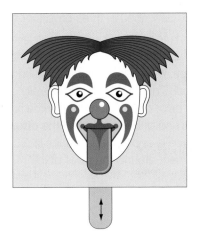

△ **Figure 10.8** Reciprocal movement

4. **Oscillating** – swinging side to side in alternate directions.

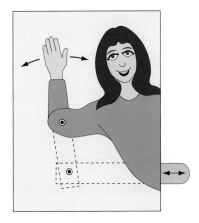

△ **Figure 10.9** Oscillating

The lever

The basic element of a mechanism is a lever. It is important that designers look at existing products and work out what mechanisms are involved in making them move. It is much easier to take an existing working idea and develop graphical ideas.

Levers are described in three orders or classes:

o **Lever 1:** the basic principles of a lever state that it is a device which pivots around a **fulcrum**. A load is applied at one end of a rigid bar. The bar is placed centrally on top of the pivot point (fulcrum). A force is applied at one end of the bar, called the **effort**. When the force is applied, this results in a single movement around the pivot point.

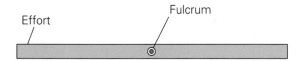

△ **Figure 10.10** Basic principles

o **Lever 2, force multiplier:** where by altering the position of the fulcrum, the effort can be multiplied and therefore a larger load lifted.

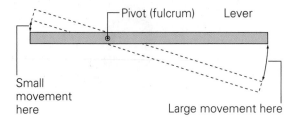

△ **Figure 10.11** Force multiplier

o **Lever 3, movement multiplier:** the effort is applied between the load and the fulcrum. The effort needed is greater than the load, and the amount of movement is multiplied.

Linkages

A linkage can act as a lever. In most cases it transfers one mechanical motion to another. A linkage is often used to connect other mechanical devices such as cams to levers or to cranks – or vice versa.

Two types of pivot are used on a linkage:

1. a fixed pivot attaches the linkage to a background

2. the movable joint joins two parts of the linkage together.

Pivots can be made from a variety of paper fasteners when making mechanisms from plastic sheet, thick paper or card.

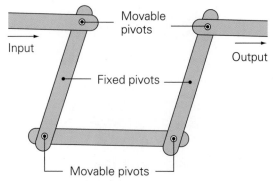

△ **Figure 10.12** Linkage fixed pivots

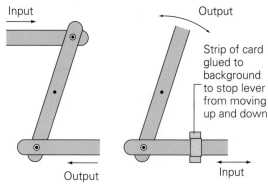

△ **Figure 10.13** Linkage brings about change in direction and movement

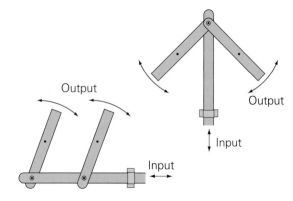

△ **Figure 10.14** Linkage with several movable parts

Components that can be used for pivots

Eyelet

Click or ratchet rivet

Paper fastener

△ **Figure 10.15** Components that can be used for pivots

Key terms

Lever – a rigid bar that can rotate around a fixed pivot.

Linkage – a mechanism involving two or more levers.

Mechanism – creates movement.

Pivot – a point of rotation.

Exam tips

- Do not always try to invent new mechanisms.
- Try to keep your mechanism simple and effective.
- Use light, rigid materials for mechanisms rather than string, heavy metals or woods.

Other useful resources

A useful internet link: http://www.print4biz. org.uk/glossary.htm

An example of a printing company which has developed the ability to produce commercial work in high definition printing: http://www. longridge.net/index.html

A large collection of useful worksheets for teachers and students: http://www. technologystudent.com

10.6 Audio/visual and programmable ICs

In modern graphical presentation there is now more use of audio/visual and programmable features that can be added by the graphic designer to appeal to the consumer. In Chapter 8 the use of graphical software and multimedia presentations are described – we can see the results of the use of these in advertising on television, big screens in town centres, and the advertising displays around football grounds.

△ **Figure 10.17** Big screen

Programmable devices are used by the graphic designer as part of the manufacturing process. Examples include Stilka and CAMM.

The programmable IC (integrated circuit) is designed to give the user a large amount of information handling in the smallest possible package. In schools, programmable ICs can be described as 'electronic chips attached to a circuit board that can be made to do different things through an attachment to a computer'. In the 'real world' the chip is hidden within the product and is designed to have limited features – for example it could make a noise or switch on a device. There are also devices that can be programmed through a series of simple switches.

There are many opportunities for a designer to incorporate a programmable ICs into point of sale or products. They can be used to play tunes, record voices, flash lights and text, or to move simple mechanisms. Examples of these devices can be found in most high streets, for example bus sign information and greeting cards that play songs.

Key terms

Programmable – an object or device that will follow instruction.

IC – integrated circuit

Audio – sound

Visual – what we can see

Summary

- o Industry usually makes products in quantity, normally batch or mass produced.
- o JIT is a more efficient production method.
- o Understand that the way in which a one-off product is made in school is different from methods used in industry.
- o Quality assurance makes sure the quality the designer wants is set out.
- o Quality control involves checks during manufacture to make sure this quality is achieved.

Exam tips

- o Do not always try to invent new mechanisms.
- o Try to keep your mechanism simple and effective.
- o Use light rigid materials for mechanisms rather than string and heavy metals and woods.
- o Consider new technology for your outcome.

chapter 11
Industrial practices

Introduction

Many of the processes, skills and techniques used in schools and colleges vary little from those used in industry. Perhaps the two most significant differences are the scale and the cost of production. In this chapter we will look at the similarities as well as the differences.

This chapter covers some very important elements – the printing processes are fundamental to graphics and as such regularly appear as questions in the exam papers. The construction of a net has long been a favourite of examiners and is the foundation of good packaging design. It is best to take this chapter in stages and carry out some of the activities, while incorporating the key points and terms into your revision sheets.

11.1 Methods of production

One-off production

In the majority of cases, students completing their GCSE work for graphics or resistant materials will make a **one-off** product. They will see it through from idea and design to making and evaluation. It will be a unique product, which will probably have been labour-intensive and relatively expensive, but these aspects are not so important when making the product for an examination. The product has the opportunity to be exceptionally well made, fit for a specific purpose and to the liking of an individual.

Key term
One-off production – the making of a single product.

Activity

Write down a list of six situations where a product is likely to be a one-off production. Explain why this is the case.

Example: a calendar containing pictures of the family and their adventures, to be given as a 60th birthday present to a grandparent. The images make this a one-off product; they have relevance for a specific situation and individuals.

Batch production

In industry it is usually necessary to make and sell more than one example of a product. This type of production is known as **batch** production. Making the product in batches means that it is possible to alter the next batch slightly, and include changes or upgrades that improve the product. This flexibility can help to prevent overproduction and financial loss, and can also cushion the potentially negative impact of fashion on the outcome.

The alterations can be carried out by someone other than the designer, and consequently will be cheaper.

Activity

Write down a list of six situations where a product is likely to be batch produced. Explain why this is the case.

Example: the leaflet for a National Trust property. These are distributed to a number of visitors upon their arrival throughout the year. Many of the properties are upgraded on an annual basis and the information becomes out of date. The leaflets can be reviewed and altered without all of the information being changed; therefore they can be described as flexible and capable of batch production.

Key term

Batch production – small 'runs' of a product; can be as few as 10 or as many as 2,000.

Mass production

This type of production deals with very large numbers of items. The labels wrapped around tins of food are mass produced; so too are widely selling magazines. In this situation the system is fully automated and expensive to set up, but will produce each unit very cheaply providing the demand is sustained.

There is no allowance for variation in the product. Many of the mass-producing machines can work all day and night without stopping, and just require people to ensure that the machines are working as they should.

Key term

Mass production – the making of thousands of the product; the machines are likely to be working for 24 hours non-stop.

Exam practice questions

1. An invitation to a party can be a one-off or a batch-produced product. Explain how this can be the case.

2. A free guide to cycling in Hertfordshire is available from the local authority. Give three reasons why this would be batch rather than mass produced.

11.2 Sequence of making tasks

When creating a product, many tasks must be completed in a predetermined sequence, so that the unit is successfully made, without any problems. This sequence will have been resolved when making the prototype (see section 11.3).

In production, the product must be checked

carefully between each of the stages, to ensure that the quality is good enough. Some manufacturers use a flow chart as their system for this type of planning. Both quality control and quality assurance procedures would have been used for this product (see section 11.7). This critical sequence will have been written down or programmed into the computer.

△ **Figure 11.1** Stage 1

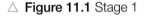

△ **Figure 11.2** Stage 2

△ **Figure 11.3** Stage 3

△ **Figure 11.4** Stage 4

△ **Figure 11.5** Stage 5

Having the wrong sequence may mean that some components cannot be fitted into the product. This would be a costly mistake: time-consuming and wasteful.

Figures 11.1 to 11.5 show a series of stages in the manufacture of a point-of-sale display. In this case, the model makers were responsible for the sequencing of the making, and the procedures for assembly were accurately recorded.

Not all of the stages are shown in the photographs. The sequence of assembly is determined and fixed by one of the supervisors.

This arrangement means that those on the production line need only worry about making their part of the display to the required standard. The supervisor will check at a variety of critical stages that the quality of outcome is as expected. All of the components for the display were made before any of the assembly started.

Activity

Using the construction of a paper aircraft, or the folding of a napkin, chart the sequence of making/folding the product. Use a series of stages which clearly illustrate the sequence.

11.3 **Making a prototype**

Depending on the sizes and the proportions of your product, it is nearly always a good idea to make a mock-up or prototype. This scale model will help to determine whether the final product functions in the way you want. The materials can be different from the final outcome, but the sections and form should be as close to the final product as possible. If you are making a mechanism for a pop-up book then you need to be sure it works. It helps to carry out the processes of manufacture, as it will identify some of the problems you are likely to encounter.

Often it is easier to make one model of the final form and another model of the mechanism included in your outcome. Take pictures of your modelling, and evaluate the outcomes as you work. Put this work in the folder to show clearly how your product developed. Write up any special points that you learned about the experience, process or material.

Figures 11.6 and 11.7 show the model makers creating a stand for the Cup-a-Soup product, and the same stand being assembled on the production line. You can see slight changes if you look closely.

△ **Figure 11.6** Model makers for the Cup-a-Soup product

△ **Figure 11.7** The product on the production line

Activity

Using a piece of A4 paper, create a birthday card for a friend. The front should have a small window so that part of the inside of the card is visible. This is intended as a prototype to work out the positioning of the window, so the text can be completed by hand.

11.4 Scale of production

The scale of production will directly influence a range of common factors:

o time
o materials
o labour
o quantity
o cost
o the type of product.

The degree to which each factor is important will dictate the method used. For example: if the product were to be a one-off, then the time taken to manufacture the item is likely to be longer and less important. Individual items often require specific problems to be resolved, can be personalised and sometimes will be constructed with greater client involvement. The materials used can be carefully selected to demonstrate a colouring or feature, or work with a particular environment in mind. It is frequently the case that the manufacturer is a highly skilled individual who works alone or with a small team of like-minded people. They are less interested in making a large number of the products, and prefer to move onto another project where the demands are different even if the processes are similar.

The costs will vary whichever method of production is used. One-off production can have high labour cost as skilled workers can demand more money. Batch production can employ jigs and templates to speed up the process, but will have large initial costs in getting the process ready for production. As long as the market can be guaranteed, then it might be better to mass produce the product, which will reduce the unit cost.

Many calculations need to be completed before the method of production is settled upon. As an individual, it is likely that you would go through the stages of one-off and batch production before even considering mass production. For a business, however, this would not be the case, as experience and expertise would rapidly influence decisions on the method of production.

11.5 Just-in-time production (JIT)

This is a way of working that is established at the factory where the product is being made. It is also known as **lean production**. This system helps to produce exactly what you want, when there is demand. You only order what you need, establish the production line, and make the product at the time of need.

The advantages are that JIT production:

o improves efficiency and therefore competitiveness
o cuts down waiting and transport costs to the smallest amount
o prevents too many products being made
o saves on materials and the money spent
o removes the concern about where or how to store the stock
o maintains the quality.

The disadvantages are that:

o the system is expensive to implement in terms of time and energy
o the supply of materials can be interrupted.

Activities

Explain and expand on the advantages of JIT production in the bullet point list above. The two disadvantages have been done for you.

1. The staff will require training. Systems will need to be devised, trialled and implemented. Existing working terms and conditions will need to be renegotiated. Where applicable, trades unions will be involved to ensure the smooth transition of working procedures.

2. In 2010 the eruption of a volcano meant that ash prevented aircraft from flying from one country to another. Supplies of materials were unable to reach some factories and production was halted.

11.6 **The making of a common graphic product**

A label for a drink container has to be designed, produced and printed. The designer of the label, probably a graphic artist, will be given a brief which will typically include the following:

○ a list of information which must be on the container
○ a theme or product identity, related to the manufacturer, perhaps including a corporate identity
○ a good idea of the target market
○ a description of the contents.

The graphic artist is also likely to be given some other information which the manufacturer will believe important.

Designing a label

A designer will probably use a software package to design a label. The artist will create a series of ideas and present the best of the selection to the client. The ideas will not only be on screen but also in model and 2D images, usually mounted for display to the client on foam board. These ideas will show the label on the container, and also a number of the containers, all with some subtle differences.

The client will make a selection based on the advice of their team and the suggestions from the graphic artist. It is quite normal for some small alterations to be made at this stage and this 'tweaking' will accommodate the agreement of all of those involved. The final design will be sent to the printer for multiple copies to be made, or managed within the manufacturer's factory.

In some cases the label will be printed directly onto a can or bottle rather than attached as a separate label. The drink will then be added to the container. The containers will be packaged for transporting and sent to the wholesaler or retailer. You and I, the consumers, will then buy the drink. Hopefully we will dispose of the empty

△ **Figure 11.8** A bottle display showing both types of labelling

container so that it can be recycled! Figure 11.8 is a small display of both types of labelling.

> **Activity**
> Using your own brief, create a label for a can of drink. Make sure that the brief is as full as possible. Present your ideas as a 2D outcome, and also wrap a copy of your printed solution around an existing can to create a more lifelike result. You can see how to make the net for the wrap-around in the section on surface developments in Chapter 4.

Designing for a one-off product

The drinks can label is a product which is likely to be mass produced. When smaller quantities are involved, the techniques of production are likely to change, depending on the product.

A party invitation is a good example of a graphic product which can be screen printed, block printed, or completed at home on the computer using a suitable software package. In this case the brief and the specification are still very important, but the ideas and development are likely to be the elements which are initially time-consuming. Once the design is determined and approved, it can be printed. If it is double-sided then the two sides must be aligned accurately so that any trimming of the card does not detract from the reverse side and any image which is printed on it. When working at home, putting card through the printer will require a change in the settings for most printers.

> **Activity**
>
> Design and make a business card suitable for a newly qualified professional person. Keep the design simple and add only essential details, using no more than two colours.
>
> Using a series of bullet points, describe how this card would be made in batches of 100.

11.7 Maintaining quality

Quality control

This is carried out by the manufacturer at every stage. Every product may not be tested but the quality is checked by sampling; perhaps one in every hundred items is checked to make sure that it is fit for purpose. This checking can be done by measurement, testing and supervision of the various processes. It is important that each of the stages is checked, as mistakes can prove to be very expensive if not rectified immediately.

For example, during the manufacture of a book, it would be important to check the consistency of the paper, the printing ink, the quality of the print, the nature of the binding, etc.

Quality assurance

This is achieved by the manufacturer when their product consistently meets a predetermined set of quality standards. It therefore offers a guarantee that the product will always perform well during use.

These standards can be set by bodies such as the International Organization for Standardization (ISO) or the British Standards Institution (BSI) who use the Kitemark as their symbol; this gives an assurance that quality, safety and value are inherent in the product. The BSI will have independently tested the product and issued a licence to the company for the manufacture of that product.

> **Key point**
>
> The differences between quality control and quality assurance are often confused.

> **Exam tip**
>
> Answers to exam questions will need to show how quality control and quality assurance are critical to the success of a product. It is always best to illustrate the answer with an example.

> **Activities**
>
> 1. Find a product which displays the Kitemark. State clearly why in this instance the users will feel reassured by the guarantee offered. Make a drawing of the Kitemark so that you can remember the shape.
>
> 2. The lion mark is the picture of the head of a lion in a yellow triangle with a green outline. This was introduced in 1988 by the British Toy and Hobby Association. Either draw or make a copy of this symbol using tracing paper. If toys are marked with this symbol, what can the consumer expect?

11.8 **Printing**

Commercial printing allows for the production of high-quality duplicates of a piece of artwork. These can be produced as leaflets, magazines, books, flyers, etc. The artwork could include the lettering and fonts that are required as well as a photographic or self-generated image.

Pre-press procedure

It is common for the artwork to be sent for printing in a digital format, usually a PDF file. On receipt of the image, the printer will prepare the image for printing. Processes in preparation to print are called **pre-press**.

The pre-press operations could include the following:

○ digitise artwork
○ artwork check
○ colour separation.

Digitise artwork

If the image is not in a digital format, the printer will convert this by scanning the image and producing a high-resolution digital image. At this stage any digital work received would be checked for compatibility with the printer's computer system.

Artwork check

The printer will check the digital artwork for flaws and accuracy. A high-quality, high-resolution photograph will give an accurate print. The image will also be checked to ensure that it is suitable for the chosen print process.

Colour separation

Printing uses four colours. When these four colours are mixed, any colour can be produced. The four colours are cyan (C), magenta (M), yellow (Y) and black (K).

Black is not really a colour, but adding it gives tone and shade to the print. The initials of the colours are used to give an abbreviation of this

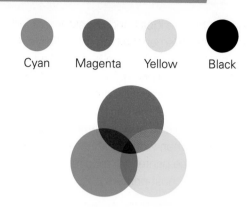

Cyan   Magenta   Yellow   Black

△ **Figure 11.9** The four colours, CYMK

process CYMK (note that it uses the last letter in the word black). When printing, the colours are not truly mixed. Each colour is printed as a tiny dot. If yellow dots are printed together they look like a block of yellow; if cyan dots are printed together they look like a block of blue. When yellow and cyan dots are printed next to each other, they look like a block of green.

△ **Figure 11.10** Dots give an impression of solid colour even though the dot spacing can be large.

Activity

Find examples of printed material. Use a magnifying glass to examine the detail. Illustrate the detail that you see.

Each of the four colours is printed in turn, and as they are layered over each other, the required colour is seen. In order for the right colour to be printed, the original artwork will be **colour separated** into the four base colours CYMK, by a computer.

Metallic and special colours will be printed over the CYMK print, as these cannot be separated in the normal way.

> ### Activity
>
> Some graphic packages you use at school or college will identify colours in both RGB (red, green, blue) and CYMK. By typing in a CYMK reference, the same colour will appear on every computer. What colours are these samples?
>
> | C | Y | M | K |
> |----|-----|----|----|
> | 48 | 0 | 84 | 0 |
> | 85 | 100 | 30 | 21 |
> | 11 | 92 | 7 | 0 |
> | 44 | 0 | 38 | 0 |
> | 62 | 86 | 0 | 0 |
>
> △ **Table 11.1** Sample colours

Printing processes

You need to be aware of five printing processes:

1. Offset lithography
2. Flexography
3. Gravure
4. Screen printing
5. Digital printing.

To choose which process is the most suitable, you need to consider these factors:

- quantity required (production run)
- what material you are printing on (weight of paper, card, plastic, etc)
- cost
- quality.

△ **Figure 11.12** A screen shot from Adobe® Photoshop® showing colour referencing

△ **Figure 11.11** The density of each colour changes to match the required blending on the final print

Offset lithography

△ **Figure 11.13** Industrial printing press

Offset lithography is the most common form of printing process. The CYMK images are transferred onto their own plates. This used to be done photographically and chemically etched; a process called **photomechanical transfer (PMT)**. Recent technology has allowed the plates to be laser-etched, which eliminates many environmental issues surrounding the disposing of chemicals and fumes. The etching is called **computer-to-plate (CTP)**; a photopolymer resin covers the plate, which hardens when the laser hits it. The untouched part of the covering can be washed away, leaving an impression of the image to be printed.

These plates are flexible and can be made from thin aluminium, plastic, card or paper. (Aluminium plates are durable and although more expensive to make, will last a long time and are suitable for large-volume print runs.) These flexible plates are wrapped around a roller. This is known as the **plate cylinder**.

The plate cylinder is in contact with two sets of rollers. The first set dampens the plate with water, the other applies the ink. Oil and water do not mix. The ink is oil-based, so it is quickly repelled from areas of the plate that have not been etched and are wet from the first set of rollers. This ink is picked up from the plate

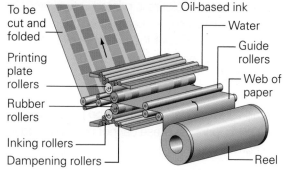

△ **Figure 11.14** An offset lithographic roller

Uses	Books, magazines, newspapers
Run size	1,000 to millions
Advantages	fast
Disadvantages	expensive set-up cost
Relative cost	medium
Print quality	very good

△ **Table 11.2** Features of offset lithography

by a second cylinder, the rubberised **blanket cylinder**. It is the blanket cylinder that rolls the image onto the paper or card.

As the printing plate does not touch the material that is being printed, the process is said to be **offset**. The printing plates are **not** a mirror image of your print, as the blanket roller reverses the final print to the correct orientation.

This process is repeated for each of the colour plates. It sounds a slow process, but industrial offset lithography printing presses are large and very fast. An image which measures one metre by half a metre can be printed 15 times per second, which is 54,000 times per hour.

A printer working this fast requires a lot of paper. The paper can be **sheet fed** or **web fed** into the machine.

Sheet feeding

Sheet feeding is like a photocopier (or a desk printer attached to your computer) in which individual sheets of paper are mechanically taken into the running press. This can be useful as it could eliminate the need of a cutting or trimming process. Sheets of paper up to A0 can be used. Sheet feeding tends to be used on smaller print runs (5,000 items); it is slower than web feed but easier to change size and styles of print jobs.

Web feeding

Web feeding is used in newspapers and magazines. It is similar to a till roll on which a receipt is printed in a supermarket. A huge roll of paper is lifted by forklift truck onto the end of the print press. This can weigh as much as a tonne, and if unrolled could stretch a mile. This is used in long print runs of over 20,000 items.

Flexography

△ **Figure 11.15** Products using flexographic printing

Flexography is very similar to offset lithography in that the CYMK four-colour process is used. However, there are some key differences.

Process is not offset

The printing plate touches the material it is printing on. This means that the image on the printing plate must be a negative of the original artwork. The printing plate is made out of a

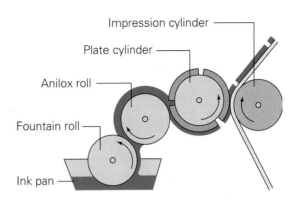

△ **Figure 11.16** The layout of the printing rollers and plates in flexographic printing

flexible photo polymer sheet which acts and looks like rubber.

The PMT (photomechanical transfer) method is used to generate the plate. A film negative is produced and UV light is shone through this onto the photo polymer. Where the UV is allowed to pass through the negative onto the plate, the material hardens. The material not touched by the UV light remains soft and can be etched away in a processing tank.

The plate is cleaned in solvents and water, and dried in an oven. This leaves the mirror image of what is to be printed standing out from the rest of the plate. The ink sits on these high bits; it is only the high bits that are printed as these are the parts that touch the printing material. This is referred to as being **in relief**. The plate is trimmed to size and attached to the printing roller, with the relief facing out.

Four cylinders

In flexography four cylinders or rollers are used. The ink roller collects the ink from the ink reservoir and places it onto the anilox roller. With a doctor blade, the anilox roller ensures that the ink is placed onto the plate cylinder in an even thickness. As all of the rollers turn, the printing material is pushed onto the plate roller by the impression cylinder. It is this pressure that ensures

Uses	Labels, plastic bags, corrugated card, foil packaging, 3D surfaces, sweet wrappers, yoghurt tops
Run size	5,000 to millions
Advantages	can print on uneven surfaces and a range of materials
Disadvantages	expensive set-up cost
Relative cost	medium/high
Print quality	good

△ **Table 11.3** Features of flexography

that the printing is even and that the ink from the plate cylinder is transferred onto the material.

Uses for flexography

As the printing plate is made from a squashy rubberised material, it allows thicker, uneven material to pass through it. Therefore flexography is ideal for printing on card, plastic or metal. These plates last a long time and are ideal for long print runs.

Gravure

Gravure is chosen when extremely high print runs of 500,000 copies or more are required; an example would be magazines included in the weekend newspapers. The set-up of the plate is very expensive, with the printing plate made out of copper or brass and the image etched into it. The deeper the etching, the more ink is placed on the paper. This method gives a good depth to the colours as the ink is placed not using dots,

but a spread of ink.

Gravure is used when printing magazines, packaging, stamps and wallpapers.

Screen printing

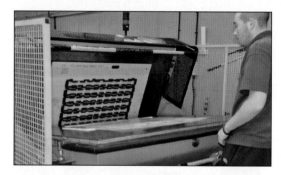

△ **Figure 11.17** A single screen printer

Screen printing is a versatile low-cost printing technique. It allows you to print on a wide range of flat materials, including paper, card, canvas, T-shirts, plastic and wood.

Uses	Magazines, labels, packaging, stamps, money, wallpaper
Run size	500,000 to millions
Advantages	very high quality print, fast printing speed
Disadvantages	expensive set-up costs
Relative cost	high
Print quality	excellent

△ **Table 11.4** Features of gravure

Screen printing can be achieved mechanically and by hand. A fine mesh is stretched over a frame. Inside this, a stencil is used to mask the areas that do not require colour. The ink is then forced through the screen with a squeegee. In the past, the screens were traditionally made out of silk, but nowadays a photosensitive nylon is used. A photonegative is placed on the screen and UV light shone through. Where the UV is exposed to the surface of the material, it hardens. As before, the excess is washed away with pressurised water jets. These gaps in the material allow the ink to flow through onto the substrate.

The four-colour process is used, so a colour separation process of the original artwork is needed. Often a fifth colour, white, is used in this process. White would usually be printed first to give a consistent base colour (when printing on brown corrugated card, for example).

The quality of finish is not as good as with lithographic processes; this, however, is compensated for by its cost efficiency and ability to print on a variety of materials.

Digital printing

Digital printing on a commercial scale is very similar to printing with a laser printer in your classroom. Ink in powder form (toner) is held in trays and applied to the paper or card with an electrostatic charge. The laser neutralises the charge on a drum. The toner only sticks where the electric charge is, and the rolling drum applies this to the paper. The toners are supplied in the CYMK colours.

The big advantage to digital printing is that it avoids the manufacture of the printing plate. This cuts down the set-up cost of the printing operation. It also means that the print can be changed quickly with little expense.

The disadvantage is that toners are expensive. This makes large production runs less cost-effective as the unit cost is high compared to other printing methods. A typical run would be up to 3,000 copies. This makes digital printing an ideal method for your school or college to use to send colourful leaflets to every parent.

Quality control

Printing can be expensive. It is important that the quality of the print is high, meaning that the last print will look exactly the same as the first one. This is vital if it is a print run of millions where a ton of paper has been used and hundreds of gallons of ink. To check that the printer is printing correctly, a system of marks is used to check accuracy and consistency:

○ registration marks
○ colour bars
○ crop marks.

Uses	Posters, T-shirts
Run size	1,000–2,000
Advantages	can print on many materials including textiles
Disadvantages	can be slow (mechanical systems are available)
Relative cost	low
Print quality	decent (not as sharp as other printing methods)

△ **Table 11.5** Features of screen printing

Uses	One-off items, small batch runs
Run size	1,000–3,000
Advantages	no set-up costs, instant one-offs
Disadvantages	expensive item cost
Relative cost	high
Print quality	good

△ **Table 11.6** Features of digital printing

Knowledge link

For more information on registration marks, colour bars and crop marks, refer to Chapter 10, page 132.

Activity

Look for print quality marks on newspapers or packaging. Cut these out and label them after you have stuck them in your exercise book.

The process of colour separation can cause common problems. When the base colour has been split into the four CYMK colours, the colours then need to be put back together accurately when printed, to give a good representation of the original colour and image.

Activity

Copy the sequences from Figure 11.18, the printing sequence diagram, onto postcards. Mix them up, then without referring to this book try to arrange the cards into the order that printing operations take place.

11.9 Print finishes

Print finishes are important to the overall look and feel of the final printed product. As the name suggests, the finishing treatment often occurs after the item has been printed. Finishing is expensive, and can be as much as the cost of the initial printing. So why do it?

- It can add to the overall quality and feel of the finished piece.
- Finishing makes the product more attractive (aesthetics).
- It can protect the product, making it more durable.

Printing sequence

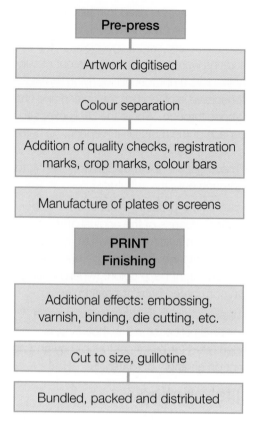

△ **Figure 11.18** A sequence diagram of the printing process

Types of print finish

The most common types of print finishes are:

- varnishing/spot varnishing
- lamination
- embossing
- foil blocking
- die cutting
- special colours.

Varnishing

Varnishing is a common technique in finishing a graphic product. Similar to varnishing in wood, it can create a gloss, satin, matt or transparent colour over the print. Varnishing adds a small layer of protection, but is often used as a decorative effect.

Varnish can be applied as a **flood coat**. In lithographic print, an extra roller to the print process can be added. (Usually the whole run is taken through a separate machine, but the principle is the same.) This coats the whole of the area with a thin layer of varnish. The print is run through UV light, which cures the varnish quickly.

Alternatively, a plate can be made to apply the varnish in specific areas of the print, like a plate for the CYMK colours. For example, you could make a logo glossy so that it has more impact. This is called **spot varnishing**.

Lamination

This process is used for the protection of a product. It can form a water-resistant, wipe-clean surface on a printed product. This is useful for menu cards to be used in a kitchen, or for a write-on, wipe-off notice board.

Lamination is a similar process to **encapsulation**. In encapsulation, the whole product (both sides) is heat-sealed in a plastic film; this is similar to the action of a desktop laminator that you may have at school or home. Industrial lamination applies plastic film to one or both sides. The process is similar: the graphic product and the PET film are squeezed through rollers, bonding the film to the surface using heat and pressure.

Embossing

Embossing changes the shape of the printed surface. A die and press are used to force the shape into the paper or card. Tonnes of pressure can be used to ensure that the effect is crisp and permanent. Embossing lifts or dips the surface of the print. This catches the light and enhances the effect of the printing.

Braille is embossed into paper to help blind people to read.

△ **Figure 11.19** Embossing raises part of the card to give a relief effect

 Activity

Find a piece of printed material that has been embossed. Place paper over this and gently rub a soft pencil over the embossed area.

Foil blocking

The manufacturing process for foil blocking is very similar to that of embossing. Pressurised dies are used to squeeze a pre-glued metallic film onto the graphic product. This gives a superb decorative effect, and is often used on Christmas cards, expensive packaging and wedding stationery.

△ **Figure 11.20** Foil blocking is frequently used on greetings cards and wedding stationery

> **Activity**
>
> Find a product which has been foil-blocked. Notice if the paper or card has been squeezed or flattened in the foil-blocked area. What do you think would have caused this?

Die cutting

Die cutting is an accurate, quick way of cutting and scoring card and paper. The principle of die cutting is similar to that of using a pastry cutter. In cooking, a sharp shaped blade is pushed through pastry; when the cutter is removed, a piece of pastry has this shape. The same is true when die cutting paper and card, although much more force and a sharper blade are needed to force its way though.

If the blade is not so sharp or rounded it will not cut through the paper/card but will leave a crease instead. This is ideal to fold along. The printer uses this process when die cutting boxes and items that are to be folded.

△ **Figure 11.21** Die cutting plates hold both the press knives and the creasing bars. The foam and rubber support the blades to give a clean cut

A die cutter has several parts:

1. a press to apply the force
2. the press forme (the plate that holds the blades)
3. a sharp cutting bar (press knives)
4. a rounded creasing bar
5. rubber blocks to protect the blades and help cutting.

Special colours

Additional colours can be added to a print run, which fall outside the CYMK range; for example, fluorescent, metallic or white inks. These colours are normally printed last and are added like a varnish on an additional roller, plate or screen, depending on the chosen printing technique.

> **Activity**
>
> Design and cut in card a net for a cube. Using the edge of a safety ruler, press hard over the fold lines. How does this help the quality of the fold?

11.10 Nets and surface development

Using a net

Nets or **surface development** is the shape cut out of a flat piece of material that can be folded into a three-dimensional shape. Nets can be drawn on many thin materials including card, paper, metal and plastic.

Nets are useful to make a quick block model, or to develop a piece of packaging. In the classroom, nets are commonly used to make boxes as a packaging item. The surface graphics are applied in the pre-folded stage as they are easier to apply. A knowledge of maths to calculate volume and sizes is useful.

Industry uses nets in a variety of ways:

- Primary and secondary packaging is often created from a flat form.
- Transportation is an expensive part of the overall cost of a product; moving flat-packed boxes helps to keep the cost down as more can be moved on a pallet or in a van.

Making a net in the classroom

In the classroom, a net can be cut out by hand with scissors or a sharp blade. When using CAD to help with the designs, a laser cutter or cutter plotter can be used. In all instances it is important that the net is drawn accurately so that it can be cut and folded precisely. Lines which are cut all the way through the material are usually identified from fold lines.

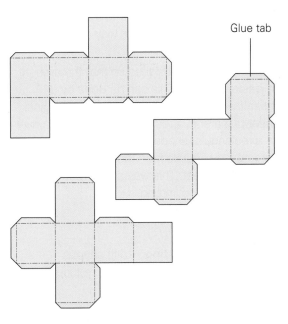

Glue tab

△ **Figure 11.22** A laser cutter

△ **Figure 11.23** A plotter cuts large sheets with a moving blade

Cut lines are drawn with a solid line; the **fold** lines with dotted line or broken line. When exporting from a CAD package to a cutter, the lines are identified by using different colours, which represent the depth of cut.

△ **Figure 11.24** A cube can be made by cutting and folding the shapes shown

Activity

Study the shapes in Figure 11.25. Draw nets for the shapes, and opening lids.

 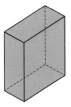  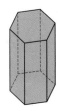 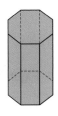

| Rectangular prism | Triangular prism | Hexagonal prism | Octagonal prism |

△ **Figure 11.25** See Activity: create nets for the shapes shown

Making a net in industry

Industrial practice is to use a **die cutter** to cut nets out. This tool stamps the shape out of its material with the use of pressure. Sharp press knives cut through the material and rounded crease blades help with the folding of material.

Die cutters can be expensive to manufacture, but are a quick and accurate way of producing nets in volume.

Industrial nets are designed so that the amount of waste is limited. This can be done by **tessellating** more than one net on the original sheet of material. Stock sheet will usually arrive as a rectangular shape. There can be a high percentage of waste from the die-cut net to the edge of the sheet. This wastage is reduced by tessellating, or optimising.

> **Key term**
>
> **Tessellating** – to fit shapes together exactly. This reduces wastage.

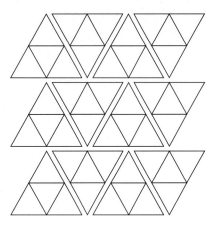

△ **Figure 11.26** When producing many of the same box, the nets are tessellated to reduce waste

CAD designs are an efficient way of producing nets. The surface development can be drawn with great accuracy and copied several times, then mirrored, flipped and rotated so that it fills the original sheet, with very few gaps between the nets.

It is usual for nets to be assembled and glued together. However, when the container is flat packed, slots and tabs are used as a method of fixing the shape. Many of the boxes in fast-food restaurants are folded by the staff on site before

your meal is delivered to the counter. Think about how much space this saves in the busy, small cooking area.

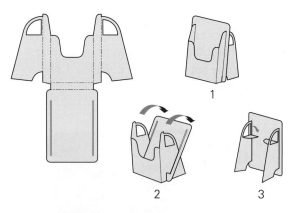

△ **Figure 11.27** The folds of a crash-bottom container hold the packaging in place without the use of glue

> **Activity**
>
> Produce a piece of packaging that can be used as a self-assembled takeaway food container. The food must be contained; no glue is to be used in the assembly.

11.11 Packaging

Most items we buy are packaged in some way. The shelves in shops and supermarkets are full of products wrapped in packaging. Products with their own natural packaging, like bananas, are packed in a tray and wrapped with cellophane.

A website selling goods will often not only display the product, but also the picture of the box in which it is packaged. This emphasises how much customers have come to rely on packaging to make choices when purchasing.

An example is the packaging of a Star Wars figure, purchased online recently by the author. The figure was sealed in a semi-rigid clear PET bubble, which was held in a folded card support to stop it from rattling around its outer box. The outer box was colour printed, with a cellophane window so the product could still be seen. The boxed product was bubble-wrapped and placed in an oversized corrugated card box. This was then covered in a grey PVC bag that was sealed and labelled with the delivery address and bar codes, so that the pack could be tracked through the delivery stage.

The small action toy was delivered in a pack over 200 times its volume! At each stage the packaging would be a cost that was passed onto the customer, more than doubling the real cost of the figure.

Packaging and its different uses

Packaging is a huge industry that supports many jobs. It also has a huge impact on the price and value of the product, and also on the environment. So why do we package? We do so in order to:

○ promote the product
○ protect the product
○ give information about the product
○ preserve the product (often food-based)
○ help stacking, storage and carrying
○ promote brand identity
○ secure the product.

> **Activity**
>
> Find a piece of packaging that uses the following key aspects of packaging: promotion, protection, information, preservation and brand identity. Label these parts and explain why and how they are used.

Packaging can be categorised as primary or secondary.

Primary packaging

Primary packaging holds the product itself. This is the package that you would see on a shelf in a shop. It will give a level of protection to the product, promote the product and also give product information.

Secondary packaging

Secondary packaging is used for the storage and transportation of goods. In the case of the Star Wars figure, this would be the bubble wrap, outer box and delivery bag. Secondary packaging is used in warehouses where lots of the same product are packed together and stacked, waiting to be distributed to shops, or opened to fill gaps in shelves.

△ **Figure 11.28** Secondary packaging protects the product before it is distributed to stores. This packaging can be labelled for handling instructions: which way up, how many can be put on top of each other

The impact of packaging on the environment

Packaging massively increases the volume of materials and processes used in making a product. Unfortunately, once we buy the product, the packaging is often discarded; 95 per cent of packaging is waste, rarely recycled and often sent to landfill. (On average a household in the UK generates one tonne of waste per year, 61 per cent of which goes into landfill.) Landfill sites are not good for the environment. As the rubbish degrades, it gives off a powerful greenhouse gas called methane. Landfills act as an indicator of how wasteful we are with the world's natural resources.

As designers, we must consider the impact of packaging on our planet. We can consider how to decrease the amount of packaging, or design in ways that will not have such a detrimental effect on the environment. If a solution is considered at the design stage, it saves money, effort and resources later on.

A WWF (Worldwide Fund for Nature) study states that if the entire world used the same amount of resources as the UK, we would use three planets' worth of resources.

The most desirable way to reduce waste is prevention, that is, not to use packaging at all. Table 11.7 shows strategies in which to control waste, from best to worst.

Figure 11.29 illustrates these strategies as a pyramid. It graphically shows which method is preferred, in terms of the best solution.

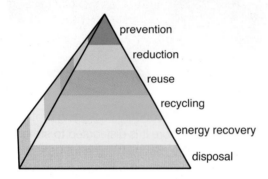

△ **Figure 11.29** The waste hierarchical pyramid illustrates how disposal causes harm to the environment

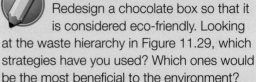

Activity

Redesign a chocolate box so that it is considered eco-friendly. Looking at the waste hierarchy in Figure 11.29, which strategies have you used? Which ones would be the most beneficial to the environment?

Walker's crisps are currently looking at changing the packets which hold their crisps. In the near future their crisp packets may be mostly made from potato starch. This would be eco-friendly in two ways: potato starch is a biodegradable material, and it is manufactured using a waste product from making the crisps.

Information contained in packaging

Key pieces of information are often found on packaging. The logo and name of the company can be used to help promote the product. The Food Safety Act 1990 makes it a legal requirement to state the content on food packaging. Food labelling must contain:

○ list of ingredients
○ percentage of food types within the product
○ energy value and protein
○ nutritional content
○ allergy content (may be traces of nuts, etc.)

Prevention	Not to use packaging
Minimisation	Reduce the amount of packaging
Reuse	Use the packaging after the product has been removed (e. g. use shoeboxes as storage boxes)
Recycle	Make the packaging out of materials that can be recycled. Remember that energy is used in the recycling of products, so although it is green, there is a cost
Energy recovery	Use waste material to fuel power stations or warm homes
Disposal	Bury the material in a landfill

△ **Table 11.7** Strategies for controlling waste

○ best before and/or use by date
○ storage instructions
○ instructions for use
○ name and address of manufacturer.

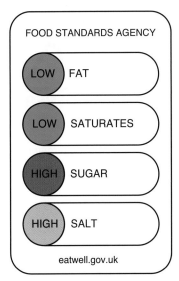

△ **Figure 11.30** Traffic lights are used on food packaging to illustrate health options (Source: Food Standards Agency)

Activity

Design a graphic system that could illustrate the eco-friendliness of a product and its packaging.

Some of the above hold true for the packaging of pharmaceutical products. It is easy to see with the level of detail and information required why packaging can be so large, even for small items.

Symbols and signs

European and international signage is used on packaging so that the product can be handled and distributed safely. This signage also gives information to the end user on disposal.

Primary packaging

On the primary package, symbols supporting the recycling and product information can often be seen. Plastics are indicated as numbers in a recycling symbol.

Safety information and warnings are also seen on primary packaging. Parental guidelines or dangers to health are often stated clearly.

Secondary packaging

On secondary packaging (the outside carton holding batches of the product), the following symbols are commonly used:

○ To be stacked this high
○ Store this way up
○ Store in the dry
○ Fragile
○ Handle with care

Activities

1. How many of the packaging symbols can you identify?
2. Illustrate and label the symbols on clothing labels. No words are used; why is this a benefit?

△ **Figure 11.31** Packaging icons are used on both secondary and primary packaging

Barcode

A barcode is also often found on packaging. This helps with the stock control in the stores, as well as being able to carry key information. Under the bar, numbers are printed which contain coded information:

Glass

Please put this in a bottle bank

Aluminium

Recyclable aluminium

Steel

Recyclable steel

Mobius Loop

This is capable of being recycled

Plastics

PETE
Polyethylene Terepthalate

HDPE
High Density Polyethylene

V
PVC

LDPE
Low Density Polyethylene

PP
Polyethylene

PS
Polystyrene

Number 7 symbol
OTHER
All other resins and multi-materials

△ **Figure 11.32** The type of plastic is identified on products with a symbol and a number; this helps recycling

1. The first two or three numbers give the country of origin.
    ○ 50 is the UK
    ○ 690–692 is China.
2. The next five numbers are the reference number of the manufacturer.
3. The last numbers are the product code from the manufacturer.

△ **Figure 11.33** Barcodes; information in stripes.

New barcodes are being developed which move away from stripes, and use colours or complex patterns. These can store thousands of times more information than conventional barcodes. In the future, an application on your phone could read a barcode and gain instructions from the information it contains.

△ **Figure 11.34** New-style barcodes can contain a huge quantity of digital information

Complex information can currently be stored in products on a **Radio Frequency Identification (RFID)** tag. This tag can be as small as a grain of rice. It is very useful during the production of a product, as it can be tracked through each stage of the product cycle. In packaging, the tag can be tracked from warehouse to store, to shelf, to sale.

Choosing materials for packaging

The selection of material is very important to the manufacture of a product. As designer, you should decide how you want the packaging to behave before you select the material. For example, a drinks container would need to be waterproof and watertight; a cereal box would need to be easily printed onto.

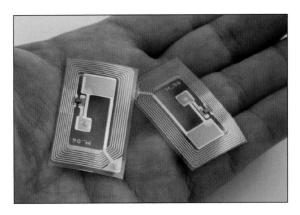

△ **Figure 11.35** RFID tags are used for security and information tracking.

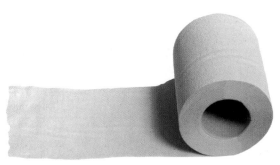

△ **Figure 11.36** Spiral-wound tubes form the card inner of a toilet roll, and have been used for packaging tennis balls and crisps

As mentioned earlier, recycling the product is a big issue. Often packaging is made from materials that can be recycled, but if two materials are combined, it is less cost-effective to recycle. For example, a card box with a PET window; these materials would need to be separated before recycling, which is a slow and expensive process.

The common materials in packaging are listed in Table 11.8 on page 160.

Some pieces of packaging are rarely seen until the product is used. A **spiral-wound tube** is found in the centre of toilet rolls and carpet rolls. This holds the product rigid as the product spools from it.

In an external form, a wound tube can be used to carry rolled-up artwork, or crisps such as Pringles. The shape of the wound card gives this structure its strength.

Security and confidence

Packets are often sealed to give confidence to the buyer that the product is new and has not been tampered with. For example, aerosol deodorants have a snap seal; if this is broken, you would know that the product has been used, or tested in the shop.

Expensive goods have security seals to indicate that the product has not been removed from the packaging, and that they are 'factory fresh'.

11.12 **Intellectual property, patents and copyright**

Intellectual property

We all know what it means to own physical items, such as iPods, cars or houses. We can understand who they belong to and when they were acquired. If something physical is stolen, it can be proven that the item is gone, and it is possible to find who has taken it.

It is also possible to own an idea or a creation. This is called **intellectual property** (IP). The proof of ownership is more difficult to prove; you may not be able to demonstrate when you first had the idea for a product. It is also more difficult to prove who thought of it first, if an idea has been stolen or independently developed.

Intellectual property can be protected from theft in several ways:

○ patent
○ copyright
○ registered and unregistered design rights.

Registered design rights vary from country to country, and national laws may not apply between different countries.

A design idea will belong to the creator unless they are working for someone or a company who is paying them for the design work. In this case,

Material	Uses	Advantage	Disadvantages	Processes
Paper, card, paperboard	Perfume packaging, food packaging, games	○ Cheap to produce ○ Can be recycled ○ Easy to print on ○ Lightweight	○ Can be crushed ○ Not waterproof	Die cutting, printing
Steels and aluminums	Drink cans, food cans	○ Strong ○ Can be recycled	○ Expensive ○ Will react to food if untreated ○ Cannot microwave ○ Expensive	Stamping, drawing, extrusion
Glass	Perfume bottles, drinks bottles, jam jars	○ Can be recycled ○ Transparent ○ Waterproof ○ Can be tinted	○ Cannot be printed on ○ Can shatter	Blow moulding
Wood	Gift boxes			CNC cut
Cellophane	Shrink wrapping	○ Clear ○ Cost-effective ○ Can seal foods	○ Not recyclable	Specialist machinery to wrap pallets, soft vacuum form over small products (multi items)
Plastics	Food packaging, bags, blister packs	○ Can be recycled ○ Transparent ○ Waterproof	○ Made from a non-sustainable source ○ Can leach toxins into food	Vacuum forming, injection moulded
Corrugated card	Secondary packaging	○ Can be printed onto ○ Light ○ Cost-effective	○ Dour appearance	Die cutting, screen printing

△ **Table 11.8** Materials used for packaging

the idea belongs to the person or company employing the person.

Patent

A patent is a way of protecting a designer's idea against someone stealing the technical and functional parts of their design. In placing a patent,

the designer must ensure that it is original and no similar patent has been placed. This patent search will take time and effort to investigate.

The criteria for a patent are that it must:

○ be new
○ have an inventive part that can be recognised by a non-expert

o be able to be industrially made

o be a physical product or process.

Once the patent is applied for, it cannot be copied in that country for 20 years. Patents after this time can be used by others. Once a patent is applied for, it is said to be in the **public domain**. After the patent has run out, anyone can develop it into a commercial and money-making product.

A granted patent can be sold to others to develop, or the royalties can be sold (if a product is sold with your patent, you would receive part of the money from the sale).

Copyright

Music, artistic work and literature cannot be covered by a patent. To ensure that the intellectual property of these is protected, a **copyright** would be granted. Items which are copyrighted can be identified by the symbol ©.

This means that the picture could not be copied, or a piece of music played in public, without the permission of the songwriter, author or artist. Copyright also applies to photographs, diagrams, logos, technical drawings and layouts of published work.

Trademark

A trademark is similar to copyright, but is specific to a company's name, logo or slogan. To show that the trademark has been registered, 'TM' is usually placed next to the print. For a logo to be licensed as a trademark, it must be original and unique.

Activity

Find three common trademarks. On a piece of paper, either use these to produce an extended drawing, or use scaling to produce larger hand-drawn copies.

Registered and unregistered design

A design can be registered to protect the shape, pattern, texture and colour of a product. It can be registered at the UK Intellectual Property Office for less than £100.

A design has unregistered design rights as soon as it is created, whether on CAD, a drawing or as it a model. Currently these rights will protect your work for 15 years. If a sketch is made, it is good practice to sign and date it as proof of your intellectual property.

However, if your work is part of a school or college project, the school or college is classed as your employer; the IP would belong to this organisation.

Activity

Write a text message that would explain the differences between copyright and patents.

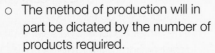

Summary

o The method of production will in part be dictated by the number of products required.

o Making a prototype helps to sort out potential problems.

o Quality must be an inherent part of a product for it to be successful.

o Different commercial printing methods are used for different applications.

o Print finishes are important to the overall look and feel of a final product.

o Product packaging promotes, protects and preserves a product, as well as providing important information about a product.

o The intellectual property of a product can be protected by patents, copyright and trademarks.

chapter 12
Controlled assessment

Learning objectives

By the end of this chapter you should have developed a knowledge and understanding of:

- o the time frames and amount of work required for the Controlled Assessment
- o the design process and how it fits with the Controlled Assessment criteria
- o the assessment criteria.

Introduction

Your AQA GCSE in Graphic Products will be assessed in two parts:

1. **A two-hour written examination worth 40 per cent of your overall GCSE.**

2. **A controlled assessment, which will take about 45 hours, making up 60 per cent of your GCSE.**

In order to achieve the best result it is important that you do as best you can in both parts of the assessment. This chapter will look at the Controlled Assessment of your GCSE.

12.1 Requirements

Controlled Assessment is a timed piece of work completed in class under supervision. The work should be your own, with a limited amount of advice and assistance. You will have about 45 hours to complete a design-and-make project.

Each candidate will choose a design brief from an area set by the examination board, and go on to produce a folder of approximately 20 A3 pages plus a manufactured outcome.

Twenty pages are enough. Remember it is not the quantity of the work, but the detail and quality of the work that count. The sheets should follow a design process. It is wise to consider the marking criteria so that the emphasis and volume of work equate to the critical points in the assessment.

During the 45 hours your teacher can only provide you with limited assistance; you should not be given specific advice on how to improve your work, or address the marking criteria. Any advice and feedback given should be of a general nature. However, you should be able to draw on all of your previous experiences of design and technology work in school, and apply your prior learning to your GCSE work.

Outside the 45 hours, research and preparation can take place. Your 45 hours will be spread over lots of lessons. It is good practice in preparation time to evaluate what you have done in the session and plan and prepare thoroughly

Key points

In summary:

- o You will have about 45 hours to design and make a design project in class.
- o The folder will be about 20 pages of A3 or equivalent.
- o You will produce a relevant three-dimensional outcome. Photographic evidence will be required.
- o The project brief will be selected by your teacher from a list provided by AQA.
- o Research can be completed outside the allocated time.
- o You and your teacher must sign a Candidates Record Form confirming it is your own work.

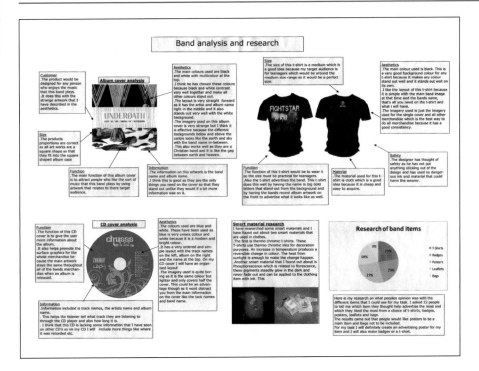

△ **Figure 12.1**

for the next time you are in the Controlled Assessment environment.

Your work will be assessed by your teacher(s). The marks will be sent to the examination board and moderated to AQA standards.

12.2 **The design process and how it fits with the Controlled Assessment criteria**

The design process is a logical sequence of events and tasks that takes and guides you through a design project. It can be seen as a continuous loop.

The Design Council uses a double diamond analogy for the process. In this it states that the designer should be thinking broadly in some parts, then narrowing down and concise and judgemental in others. The four phases of the double diamond are:

1. Discover – broad – find out the problems and research.

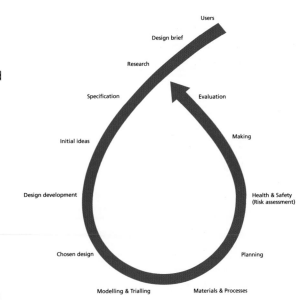

△ **Figure 12.2** The design process

2. Define – narrow – decide what is relevant, focus on the important bits.

3. Develop – broad – a wide range of ideas and opportunities.

4. Deliver – narrow – select which idea to make. Choose materials and manufacture.

More information and reading on this can be found on the Design Council's website: http://www.designcouncil.org.uk.

In this chapter we will follow the process loop in relation to the Controlled Assessment and look at how marks can be gained against the assessment criteria.

AQA will write a list of design briefs. Your teacher might select which ones would be the most appropriate for you and your class based upon facilities available. The brief is the starting point from which you can base your design.

The brief

The brief is a short statement that gives an outline of what is to be considered for your project. From the brief you can plan your research in order to work out the important key facts about your project.

12.3 **The assessment**

Your project is split into several areas for assessment purposes. A good project will have detail and work in each of these areas. The areas set by AQA are shown in Table 12.1.

> ### Knowledge link
> The knowledge and understanding found in other chapters of this book is very relevant and will help you with your Controlled Assessment work.

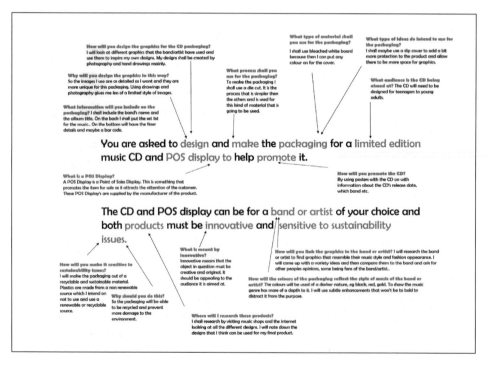

You are asked to design and make the packaging for a limited edition music CD and POS display to help promote it.

The CD and POS display can be for a band or artist of your choice and both products must be innovative and sensitive to sustainability issues.

△ **Figure 12.3** A design brief page

Assessment criteria	Maximum mark	Percentage
Investigating the design context	8	9%
Development of design proposal, including modelling	32	34%
Making	32	34%
Testing and evaluation	12	14%
Communication	6	9%
Total	**90**	**100%**

△ **Table 12.1** The assessment criteria

Each of the above sections has assessment statements attached to it. If your work 'best fits' each of the statements then you will be awarded the marks. In the next section we will look at what these statements mean and how to best show evidence of these in your project.

Investigating the design context

The statements for Investigating the design context are shown in Table 12.2.

Criterion 1 mark band	Investigating the design context
7–8	○ Discrimination shown when selecting and acquiring relevant research that will promote originality in designing ○ Excellent understanding and analysis of the design context ○ Detailed analysis of relevant existing products or systems undertaken related to design intentions ○ Comprehensive analysis of relevant and focused research undertaken ○ Clear and specific design criteria identified, reflecting the analysis undertaken ○ Target market identified and the intended consumer/user profiled
5–6	○ Good understanding and analysis of the design context ○ Good analysis of relevant products or systems undertaken ○ Good analysis of relevant research and context ○ Design criteria which reflect the analysis undertaken ○ Target market for product has been identified
3–4	○ Basic understanding and analysis of the design context ○ Some analysis of related products or systems undertaken ○ Made a superficial analysis of most of the research material and the context ○ Design criteria reflect most of the analysis undertaken ○ Some consideration has been taken of the likely consumer/user

△ **Table 12.2** Investigating the design context   *Cont.*

Criterion 1 mark band	Investigating the design context
0–2	○ Limited understanding or analysis of design context ○ Minimal analysis of other products or systems undertaken ○ Provided little evidence of research and analysis of context ○ Design criteria are very general and lacking in any detail ○ Limited understanding of the target market/user evident

△ **Table 12.2** Investigating the design context

To achieve a mark in the highest band of this criterion you could consider including the following in your work.

Show evidence of using a range of research strategies. These could include any of the following long list:

○ surveys
○ disassemblies of existing products
○ a range of existing products or systems identified and deconstructed
○ user profiles
○ selective cuttings from magazines and catalogues, stating their relevance to your project
○ a questionnaire on the problem
○ graphs and pie charts of data that you have gathered from your questionnaire
○ letters to companies and societies and responses to these letters
○ drawings of methods used to fix parts together
○ details of how to construct a pop-up
○ a review of the suitable colours, materials and costs likely to be used.

Collecting all this data is not the end of the process. You must go on to:

○ analyse the information you have collected
○ identify the useful elements
○ **keep the useful and leave out the rest**

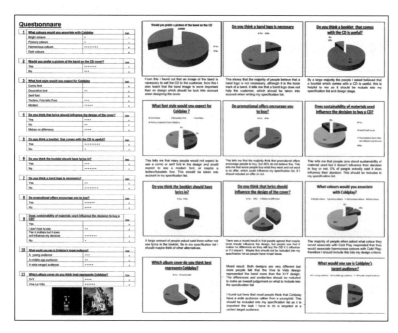

△ **Figure 12.4** Questionnaire results

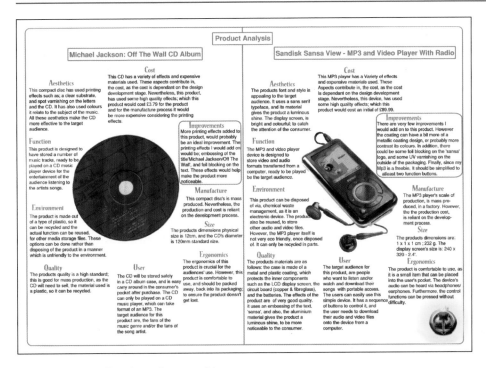

Product Analysis

Michael Jackson: Off The Wall CD Album

Aesthetics
This compact disc has used printing effects such as; a clear substrate, and spot varnishing on the letters and the CD. It has also used colours it relate to the subject of the music. All these aesthetics make the CD more effective to the target audience.

Function
This product is designed to have stored a number of music tracks, ready to be played on a CD music player device for the entertainment of the audience listening to the artists songs.

Environment
The product is made out of a type of plastic, so it can be recycled and the actual function can be reused, for other media storage files. These options can be done rather than disposing of the product in a manner which is unfriendly to the environment.

Quality
The products quality is a high standard; this is good for mass production, as the CD will need to sell, the material used is a plastic, so it can be recycled.

Cost
This CD has a variety of effects and expensive materials used. These aspects contribute in, the cost, as the cost is dependant on the design development stage. Nevertheless, this product, has used some high quality effects; which this product would cost £3.79 for the product and for the manufacture process it would be more expensive considering the printing effects.

Improvements
More printing effects added to this product, would probably be an ideal improvement. The printing effects I would add on would be; embossing of the title 'Michael Jackson/Off The Wall', and foil blocking on the text. These effects would help make the product more noticeable.

Manufacture
This compact disc's is mass produced. Nevertheless, the production and cost is reliant on the development process.

Size
The products dimensions physical size is 12cm, and the CD's diameter is 120mm standard size.

Ergonomics
The ergonomics of this product is crucial for the audiences' use. However, this product is comfortable to use, and should be packed away, back into its packaging; to ensure the product doesn't get lost.

User
The CD will be stored safely in a CD album case, and is easy carry around in the consumer's pocket after purchase. The CD can only be played on a CD music player, which can take format of an MP3. The target audience for this product are, the fans of the music genre and/or the fans of the song artist.

Sandisk Sansa View - MP3 and Video Player With Radio

Aesthetics
The products font and style is appealing to the target audience. It uses a sans serif typeface, and its material gives the product a luminous shine. The display screen, is bright and colourful; to catch the attention of the consumer.

Function
The MP3 and video player device is designed to store video and audio formats transferred from a computer, ready to be played be the target audience.

Environment
This product can be disposed of via, chemical waste management, as it is an electronic device. The product also be reused, to store other audio and video files. However, the MP3 player itself is not very eco friendly, once disposed of. It can only be recycled in parts.

Quality
The products materials are as follows: the case is made of a metal and plastic coating, which protects the inner components such as the LCD display screen, circuit board (copper & fibreglass), and the batteries. The effects of the product are of very good quality. it uses an embossing of the text, 'sansa', and also, the aluminium material gives the product a luminous shine, to be more noticeable to the consumer.

Cost
This MP3 player has a Variety of effects and expensive materials used. These Aspects contribute in, the cost, as the cost is dependant on the design development stage. Nevertheless, this device, has used some high quality effects; which this product would cost an initial of £89.99.

Improvements
There are very few improvements I would add on to this product. However the coating can have a bit more of a metallic coating design, or probably more contrast its colours. In addition, there could be some foil blocking on the 'sansa' logo, and some UV varnishing on the outside of the packaging. Finally, since my Mp3 is a freebie, it should be simplified to atleast two function buttons.

Manufacture
The MP3 player's scale of production, is mass produced, in a factory. However, the the production cost, is reliant on the development process.

Size
The products dimensions are: 1 x 1 x 1 cm ; 232 g. The display screen's size is: 240 x 320 - 2.4".

Ergonomics
The products is comfortable to use, as it is a small item that can be placed into the user's pocket. The device's audio can be heard via headphones/ earphones. Furthermore, the control functions can be pressed without difficulty.

User
The target audience for this product, are people who want to listen and/or watch and download their songs with portable access. The users can easily use this simple device. It has a sequence of buttons to control it, and the user needs to download their audio and video files onto the device from a computer.

△ **Figure 12.5** Product disassembly

Knowledge link
Pages 70–71 in Chapter 4 will help you with how to present your results from questionnaires and surveys in graphical form.

○ display the relevant information to show why it is to be used.

○ show why your choices are suitable for your project and the user. There is no need to include the original materials, just the conclusions you have reached based on the available evidence.

The data must be specific for your project. So if you were considering who will use the product, then it should be not just the end user, but the person who assembles it, delivers it and manufacturers it.

Potentially this is a massive task and could run into pages and pages. Don't let it: remember you have to try to keep the whole project to about 20 pages of A3. (If we were to apply a formula of percentage of marks awarded to sheets used,

this whole section would need to be completed in two pages.) Keep it succinct, relevant and looking good!

It is a graphics course, so presentation does matter. If you go beyond four pages then you need to look again at your work.

A question to ask yourself is 'So what?' 'I have found that creases are used in pop-up card mechanism. So what?' 'This means that on my design if I use creases the mechanism will work more efficiently and the folds will look neat and crisp.' Use the research that will help inform changes and will clearly link to and influence the outcome of your design.

Give a concise summary of what you have found and how this could be useful to you as the designer.

Clearly state who your target market is. A mood board of your target market's likes and influences

△ **Figure 12.6** Research page

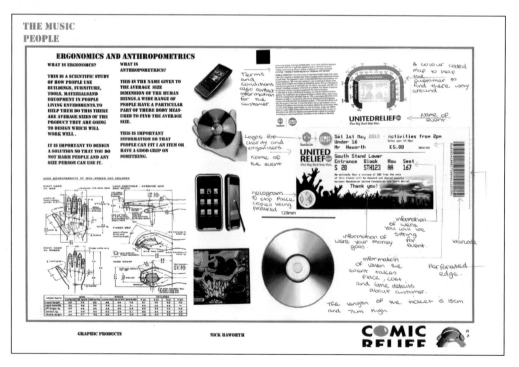

△ **Figure 12.7** Research page

could help with giving your product a visual flavour that would attract the market concerned.

Knowledge link

The information on target markets on pages 38 and 39 of Chapter 4, and on the needs and wants of customers on pages 82–83 of Chapter 5 will be useful when investigating the design context.

Write out a specification (word process this and it can save you time at the end of the project).

A specification is a clear list of what your product will do. It should be able to fit on half of an A3 piece of paper. The specification should cover approximately ten main statements that relate to your design. These can be placed into categories and an acronym – CAFÉ QUES – can be used to help you remember these. You will need to make decisions based on the following statements:

C – Cost. How much should your product retail for? Cost could have a big influence on the type of material you choose to use.

A – Aesthetics. Aesthetics is how a design looks. A design could be in the style of a design movement, an artist or a theme. It will be influenced by colour, texture, tone and proportion.

F – Function. What is the product expected to do? These should be obvious statements, kept to the three most important points.

E – Ergonomics. How can the product fit with your target market's anthropometric data? How will the product fit in with the human factors?

Q – Quality. How will your product be designed to ensure top quality in the making and its use? Must it match any quality standards?

U – User. How the product will match specific requirements of the target market and specific user.

E – Environment. What are the environmental and sustainable issues that your product should address?

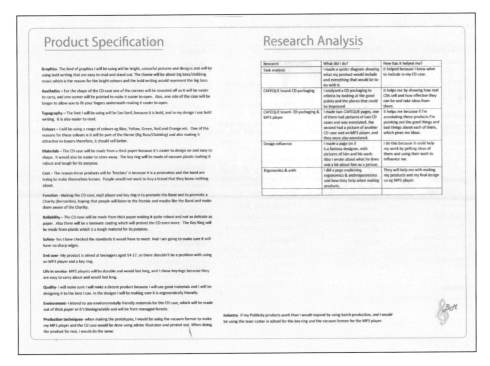

△ **Figure 12.8** Specification

C COST The cost is reasonable at £10 to £15 pounds for a astounding 3d colour scheme .it has some beautiful printing effects like the embossing,foil blocking and more.

A AESTHETICS 4 tone fading of the blues give it an eye catch cover.you bound to see immidietly you make contact with the blues.i personally havent heard it but i've told that it's amazing the font shows a wild side .

F FUNCTION the hold and protect the murchendise.in this case the cd ,It also used for advertisement and product information.

E ERGONOMICS it is very simple to use yet it has not got an easy accesible case for baby or young children to damage the cd or even cut or hurt themselves on it.

Q QUALITY the quality is great,the materials used are plastic(polystyrene high impact) and card.you can see as I mentioned before the printing effects has made it stand out aswell as the colour scheme.

U USER this product is focused at people or the public aged from round 10 to 25 roughly and any other general public is it appropriate I dont know any one s taste but to me, yes it appropriate.

E ENVIRONMENTAL IMPACT it has very little impact on the environment,and i can ensure you it can be recycle in terms of the card and maybe the plastic.

M Manufacturing it is manufactored in mass production,the techniques used are vacuum forming.leaf-lets for inside are printed and folded the inserted into th cd case

S SAFETY It is completly safe it no shar edges ,the case has an easy accesible case .but from childre under the ages 3 it is unable to be opened due to the anti lock system encorparated into it.

U USER this product is focused at people or the public aged from round 10 to 25 roughly and any other general public is it appropriate I dont know any one s taste but to me, yes it appropriate.

E ENVIRONMENTAL IMPACT it has very little impact on the environment,and i can ensure you it can be recycle in terms of the card and maybe the plastic.

M Manufacturing it is manufactored in mass production,the techniques used are vacuum forming.leaf-lets for inside are printed and folded the inserted into th cd case

S SAFETY It is completly safe it no shar edges ,the case has an easy accesible case .but from childre under the ages 3 it is unable to be opened due to the anti lock system encorparated into it.

C CONCLUSION This has helped by allowing me to learn what features should be put on a CD cover and how to improve it by making it safer or taking out sharp parts and making it a safer product for the consumer.

C COST The cost is reasonable at £10 to £15 pounds for a astounding red and a rather bewildering background .it has some beautiful printing effects like the embossing,print screening and more.

A AESTHETICS 3 tone fading of the reds give it an eye catch cover.you bound to see immidietly you make contact with the colour scheme I personally heard it and it's amazing, the font shows a wild side which is also brought out in some of the songs.

F FUNCTION the hold and protect the murchendise.in this case the cd ,It also used for advertisement and product information.

E ERGONOMICS it is very simple to use yet it has not got an easy accesible case for baby or young children to damage the cd or even cut or hurt themselves on it.

Q QUALITY the quality is great,the materials used are plastic(polystyrene high impact) and card.you can see as I mentioned before the printing effects has made it stand out aswell as the colour scheme.

△ **Figure 12.9** CAFÉ QUES

Specification List

The artist that I am designing a complete set of publicity material for is Lady Gaga. The products may meet the following design criteria:

CD Jewel Case

Function:
• Promote the CD
• Promote the band/artist
• Protect the CD
• Packaging for the CD due to transportation

Aesthetics:
• Use appropriate font styles for the CD cover design
• Use appropriate colours for the CD cover design
• Use appropriate imagery for the CD cover design

Dimensions:
• Fit the CD (140mm x 123mm)

Information:
• Name of the artist
• Track names
• Name of record label and logo
• Barcode

Materials:
• Have a good surface to print onto

POS Display

Function:
• Inform
• Have good stability
• Promote the CD
• Promote the band/artist

Aesthetics:
• Use appropriate font styles for the CD cover design
• Use appropriate colours for the CD cover design
• Use appropriate imagery for the CD cover design

Dimensions:
• Large enough to consist of the other four publicity materials

Information:
• Release date
• Name of the artist
• Name of the album
• Record label name and logo
• 'Pre-order your copy now'

Materials:
• Have a good surface to print onto

Backstage Pass

Function:
• Allow its holders to go backstage
• Promote the band/artist
• Promote the CD

Aesthetics:
• Use appropriate font styles for the CD cover design
• Use appropriate colours for the CD cover design
• Use appropriate imagery for the CD cover design

Dimensions:
• 90mm x 118mm

Information:
• Name of the artist
• Name of the album
• Barcode

Materials:
• Have a good surface to print onto

T-shirt

Function:
• Promote the CD
• Promote the band/artist

Aesthetics:
• Use appropriate font styles for the CD cover design
• Use appropriate colours for the CD cover design
• Use appropriate imagery for the CD cover design

Dimensions:
• The design for the t-shirt will be done in a printable area of 210 x 295 mm.

Information:
• Name of the artist
• Name of the album
• Record label and logo?

Materials:
• A strong yet comfortable material, for example, cotton
• Have a good surface to print onto

Badge

Function:
• Promote the CD
• Promote the band/artist

Aesthetics:
• Use appropriate font styles for the CD cover design
• Use appropriate colours for the CD cover design
• Use appropriate imagery for the CD cover design

Dimensions:
• Preferable medium-sized, so you can actually see it without it being far too big.

Information:
• Name of the artist
• Name of the album

Materials:
• The material on the top layer will be acetate, the middle layer will be paper that I have drawn my design onto and the bottom layer will be metal.

△ **Figure 12.10** Specification

S – Size. How big should the product be? These could be general – 'to fit on a table', 'to be seen from a certain distance', etc. – or they might be very specific.

Outside the CAFÉ QUES acronym you could also add social and moral issues, deadlines, and manufacturing constraints.

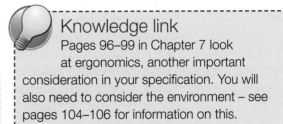

Knowledge link

The information on quality in Chapter 5 will help you consider this as part of your specification. The discussion on understanding the needs and wants of customers in Chapter 5 is also important as you will need to consider the user in your specification.

Remember that the specification is a list of requirements that your product should have. It should not give the answer to your problem.

For example, if you were designing a new piece of packaging, at this stage you should not state that it is a bag, as this would limit the opportunity to consider boxes, tins, bubbles, etc.

Knowledge link

Pages 96–99 in Chapter 7 look at ergonomics, another important consideration in your specification. You will also need to consider the environment – see pages 104–106 for information on this.

Development of design proposals

In this section of your folder you are expected to have a large range of initial design concepts and develop these into a final product.

The assessment criteria are given in Table 12.3.

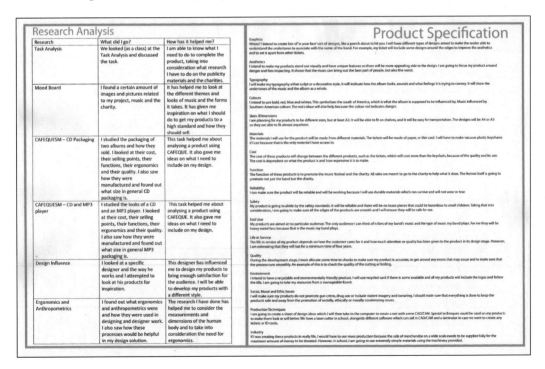

△ **Figure 12.11** Research analysis

Criterion 2 mark band	Development of design proposals (including modelling)
26–32	○ Imaginative and innovative ideas have been developed, demonstrating creativity, flair and originality. Further developments made to take account of ongoing research ○ A coherent and appropriate design strategy, with clear evidence of a planned approach adopted throughout ○ The implications of a wide range of issues including social, moral, environmental and sustainability, are taken into consideration and inform the development of the design proposals ○ Excellent development work through experimentation with a wide variety of techniques and modelling (including CAD where appropriate) in order to produce a final design solution ○ Appropriate materials/ingredients and components selected with full regard to their working properties ○ Fully detailed and justified product/manufacturing specification, taking full account of the analysis undertaken
19–25	○ Imaginative ideas demonstrating a degree of creativity, which are further developed to take account of ongoing research ○ An appropriate design strategy, with evidence of planning, adopted for most aspects ○ Development of design proposals take into account the main aspects relating to a variety of social, moral, environmental and sustainability issues ○ Good development work achieved through working with a variety of techniques and modelling (including CAD where appropriate) ○ Appropriate materials/ingredients and components selected with regard to their working properties ○ Product/manufacturing specification is complete and reflects key aspects of the analysis undertaken
12–18	○ Design ideas show some degree of creativity and further development ○ An appropriate design strategy, with some evidence of planning adopted for some aspects ○ Developments of design solutions are influenced to some extent by factors relating to social, moral, environmental and sustainability issues ○ Adequate development work achieved through working with a range of techniques and modelling (including CAD where appropriate) ○ Materials/ingredients and components selected with some regard to their working properties ○ Product/manufacturing specification reflects most aspects of the analysis

△ **Table 12.3** Development of design proposals   *Cont.*

Criterion 2 mark band	Development of design proposals (including modelling)
6–11	<ul><li>Ideas show some variation in approach or concept</li><li>A limited design strategy, with minimal planning, is evident</li><li>Some consideration taken of social, moral, environmental and sustainability issues in development of design solutions</li><li>Development work is lacking in detail but makes reference to a number of</li><li>techniques and modelling (including CAD where appropriate)</li><li>Materials/ingredients and components selected with limited regard to their working properties</li><li>Limited product/manufacturing specification which reflects most obvious features of analysis</li></ul>
0–5	<ul><li>Ideas are lacking in imagination with minimal development or further research</li><li>Little evidence of a logical approach being adopted, with no indication of planning</li><li>Development work shows little consideration of social, moral, environmental and sustainability issues</li><li>Basic development work undertaken using a limited range of techniques</li><li>Materials/ingredients and components selected with little regard to their working properties</li><li>Produced a simple product/manufacturing specification which is general in nature</li></ul>

△ **Table 12.3** Development of design proposals

This section is the creation of your ideas through to the final design. It is important to remember that this is not just drawing your concepts, but also using models to further develop and test your thinking and ideas, evidence that you have planned your project and have produced a detailed manufacturing specification and production plan.

> **Knowledge link**
> You will need to have an understanding of the drawing techniques in Chapter 4 to draw the concepts for your design ideas.

At this point a planning chart for the project could be completed. A time plan will highlight that you have considered the time frame of the whole project and have recognised all of the tasks that you need to complete. In a Controlled Assessment situation this is particularly important as this should be used to ensure that you complete the project on time. If used correctly, the time plan can also help in informing you what preparation is needed for each lesson and as a prompt to ensure you have the right tools, equipment and materials available for you to complete the tasks in the allotted time.

Your initial idea sheets are an opportunity for you to show how you think and how creative you can be. You should show that you can think of several (five or six) different ideas. These can include thumbnail sketches but the whole section should be seen as an opportunity to highlight your communication skills.

Use recognised drawing styles to illustrate your ideas; this could include isometric and perspective drawings. Use close-ups to detail parts of your design. By using sectional views and cut-aways would your concept be better explained?

Gannt chart

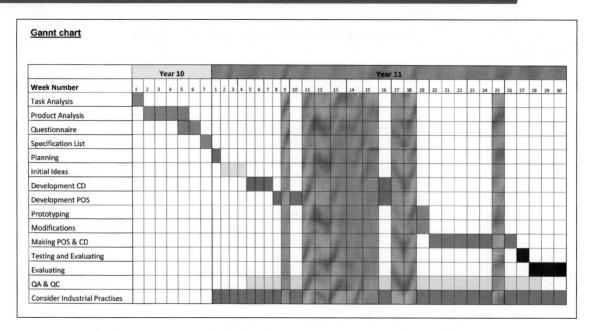

Week Number	Year 10							Year 11																													
	1	2	3	4	5	6	7	1	2	3	4	5	6	7	8	9	10	11	12	13	14	15	16	17	18	19	20	21	22	23	24	25	26	27	28	29	30
Task Analysis																																					
Product Analysis																																					
Questionnaire																																					
Specification List																																					
Planning																																					
Initial Ideas																																					
Development CD																																					
Development POS																																					
Prototyping																																					
Modifications																																					
Making POS & CD																																					
Testing and Evaluating																																					
Evaluating																																					
QA & QC																																					
Consider Industrial Practises																																					

△ **Figure 12.12** Gantt chart production plan

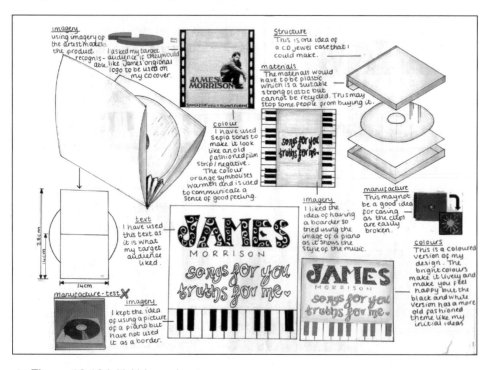

△ **Figure 12.13** Initial ideas sheet

All of the above should be annotated to give a clear understanding of your thinking process. Some of the key aspects, of your reasoning will be related to the specification, the user requirement, materials and manufacturing, ergonomics and sustainability issues. To highlight to your teacher that you have considered these aspects, try to colour code each criterion, or have clear headings to illustrate which design reasoning point you are discussing.

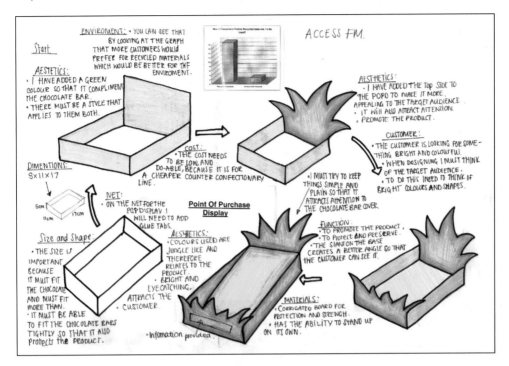

△ **Figure 12.14** The student has used the acronym ACCEESS FM to annotate the ideas, rather than CAFÉ QUES. Both ways are valid. ACCEESS FM stands for Aesthetics, Customer, Cost, Ergonomics, Environmental, Safety, Size, Function and Materials.

Exam tip

A small choice of materials drawn next to your ideas is a good way to show how you have compared materials. A reason for choice of selection next to this further illustrates your knowledge and understanding.

Knowledge link

Chapter 6 will help you with how to evaluate your designs against the specification and how to refine your ideas (see pages 87–90).

From your initial ideas choose two concepts that could be taken forward. These proposals should be illustrated with more care and detail. Show your proposal from several views. Consider form, aesthetics and proportion.

During your analysis of these initial designs you will find that your ideas do not always meet the points of the specification; problems will be found. At this point make sketches of the solutions to these issues to support your reasoning in the design process.

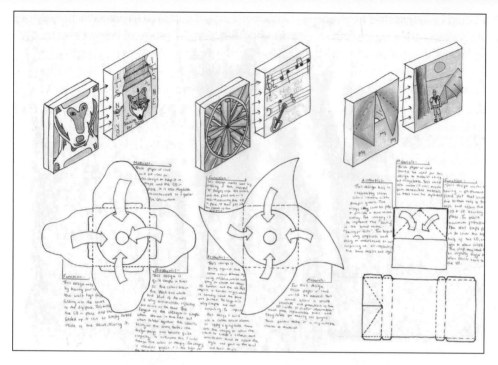

△ **Figure 12.15** Developing ideas

△ **Figure 12.16** On this work sheet the candidate has used yellow sticky notes for comments referencing specification points and blue sticky notes for the client's views

Computer-Aided Design (CAD) is an important tool in the designer's skill set. If you have these resources available to you they should be used in this section.

Three-dimensional modelling can have the advantage of being used to produce final design renderings, dimensioned workshop drawings and the cutting files for CNC machines. This stage takes up a lot of time, so remember you only have 45 hours to produce your task. It is important that you work efficiently in the time allowed.

Knowledge link

Pages 107–113 of Chapter 8 explore how to use CAD in designing. This information will be useful for your Controlled Assessment. Pages 114–116 explore how CNC machines can be used for modelling.

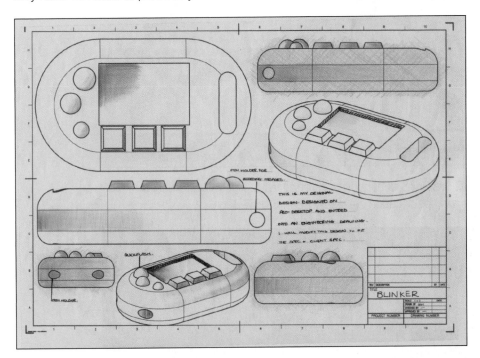

△ **Figure 12.17** CAD drawings have been worked with colour pencil to enhance and detail a design

Modelling is an intrinsic part of this section. This can be CAD models, 2D card models, or quick block models. In order to achieve the higher level of assessment it should be evidenced that you have used these models to inform, change and develop your design.

Models are very often quick 3D pieces made of card or Styrofoam™. These will not be sent to the moderator, so it is vital that photographic evidence is supplied. This has an advantage that the same photographs can be placed in your

Knowledge link

The information on sheet and block modelling on pages 13–17 of Chapter 1, and the information on modelling, mock-ups and prototypes on pages 36–38 of Chapter 2 is also relevant to your Controlled Assessment work.

folder. Sketching changes on a photograph is a clear way of showing changes that you intend to make to your design.

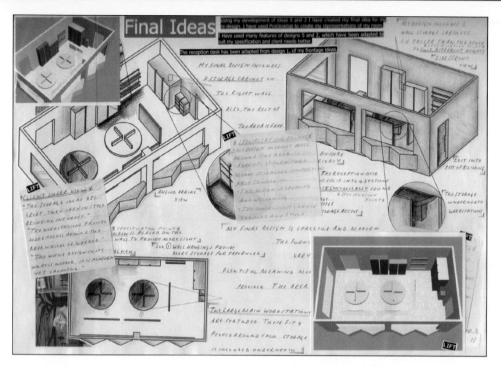

△ **Figure 12.18** CAD drawings enhanced and rendered to illustrate the design. Notes referring to the specification are easily seen on the page

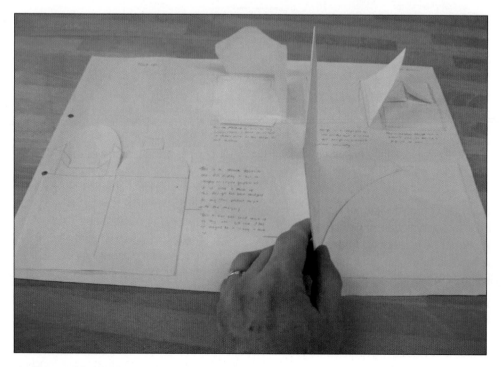

△ **Figure 12.19** 2D test pieces in the folder are an efficient way of modelling

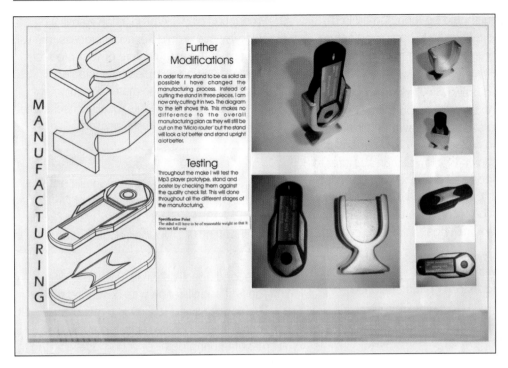

△ **Figure 12.20** Models made on the CNC router will take time to finish in detail

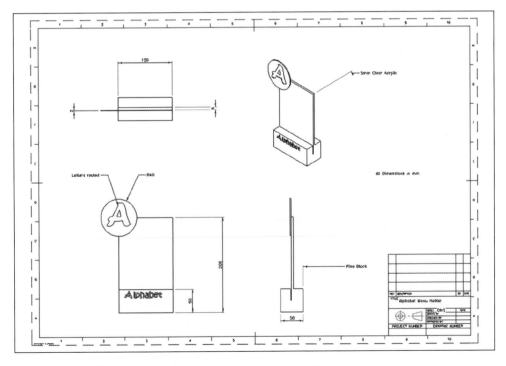

△ **Figure 12.21** A dimensioned drawing in orthographic projection

Your final design should be represented in a way that means a third party can manufacture your design. Three of the common methods of achieving this are:

1. Dimensioned drawing – Producing your final design in an orthographic drawing. The drawing should be drawn in third-angle orthographic projection. Six key dimensions should be shown to allow a manufacturer to recognise sizes and produce your concept. Don't forget to add the scale used. Material and production techniques can be noted on the workshop drawings.

> ### Knowledge link
> The information on dimensioned drawing on pages 59–60 of Chapter 4 will help you with this.

2. Production plan – A production plan is a stage-by-stage guide of every process that will be used in the manufacture of your product. The plan can be completed as a table. Headings must include material, equipment used, safety requirements, quality checks and – very importantly – time allocation.

> ### Knowledge link
> You will need to include details of materials (see Chapter 1), equipment (see Chapter 2), Safety (see Chapter 9) and quality (see Chapter 10) in your production plan.

3. A second specification is key at this point. The first specification was described earlier. The second specification is a manufacturing specification. Create a table to show the manufacturing detail of your model and the manufacturing detail of your product, should it be commercially manufactured.

Plan Of Making

Date.	The product or component.	Description of task.	Justify why the task needs to be in this position in your plan.	List the tools, processes and materials required.	H&S	Quality control.	Est. time needed
Mon. 28/1	The molded section of the digipak	I will process the Solid works prototypes	This will determine the exact size of the surrounding card	Solid Works	None	I will use smart Dimension to ensure correct dimensions are used.	30 mins
Mon. 28/1	The molded section of the digipak	I will Rapid Prototype the molded section	This is the next stage after the processing of the job	Solid Works File, Rapid Prototype Machine.	None	I will check the quality of the product once it is made.	1 hour
Thurs. 31/1	The Digipak	I will set up the document size to fit the molded section and design the surface graphics	The size of the finished molded section will determine the document size	Fireworks, 2D Design	None	I will double check the dimensions of the front, back and spine	4 Hours
Mon. 4/2	The Digipak	I will then print a B&W proof	The printing process naturally follows the design process	Fireworks and B&W printer, mat, craft knife and safety rule	Cutting Activity	I will check the proof against the molded section. Additional use of crop marks and bleed area	30 mins
Mon. 4/2	The Digipak	I will then print the design on board and in colour	The job follows the B&W proof	200 gsm gloss board, Fireworks and a colour printer	None	Use of crop marks and bleed area	20 mins
Mon. 4/2	The Digipak	I will then score the fold lines for the spine.	These will be done before cutting the crop marks - (Removing the crop marks will remove the trim marks)	Roland Camm1	Cutting Activity	Use of crop marks and bleed area	5 mins
Thurs. 7/2	The Digipak	I will then cut out the design	The crop marks must be cut after the scoring	Roland Camm1	Cutting Activity	Use of crop marks and a bleed area	10 mins
Thurs. 7/2	The complete product	I will join the two components together	This is the final stage of the making	Double sided sticky tape, craft knife, scissors	Use of a craft knife	Carefully check the two components are aligned before bonding them together	10 mins
Thurs. 7/2	The complete product	I will trim any over-hangs	The two components needed to be bonded first	A craft knife, mat and safety rule	Use of a craft knife	Check the quality of the product after trimming has taken place	5 min

△ **Figure 12.22** Production plan

Knowledge link
Pages 137–143 of Chapter 11 gives details of methods of production. The industrial practices described in Chapter 11 will help you with your second specification.

Points to consider:

○ Materials that you have used in the class and materials to be used commercially. For example, you may have used thin HIPs to vacuum form a part on your model. Commercially, acrylic could be used to give a higher polish to the edges.

Knowledge link
A good understanding of materials and their properties is needed so you can make these decisions. Chapter 1 will help you with this.

○ Techniques that you have used in your realisation model and commercial manufacturing techniques. An example for this would be that if you used an inkjet printer to produce the visuals, commercially on a large print run lithographic printing could be used.
○ Printing effects, like blocking or lamination.
○ Predicted costs. Consider the cost of materials you have used and how these may change for large-scale manufacture, including the set-up costs of machines, tooling and the advantage of buying materials in bulk.

Knowledge link
See pages 144–152 of Chapter 11 for details of printing and print finishes.

Making

Criterion 3 mark band	Making
26–32	○ Final outcome(s) show(s) a high level of making/modelling/finishing skills and accuracy ○ Selected and used appropriate tools, materials and/or technologies including, where appropriate, CAM correctly, skilfully and safely ○ Worked independently to produce a rigorous and demanding outcome ○ Quality controls are evident throughout the project and it is clear how accuracy has been achieved. ○ The outcome has the potential to be commercially viable and is suitable for the target market

△ **Table 12.4** Making

Cont.

Criterion 3 mark band	Making
19–25	○ Final outcome shows very good level of making/modelling/finishing skills ○ Selected and used appropriate tools, materials and/or technologies including, where appropriate, CAM correctly and safely ○ Outcome demonstrates a high level of demand ○ Quality control checks applied in the manufacture of the product ○ The outcome is suitable for the target market and could be commercially viable with further development
12–18	○ Final outcome shows good level of making/modelling/finishing skills ○ Used appropriate materials, components, equipment and processes correctly and safely (including CAM) ○ Parts of outcome show high levels of demand ○ Applied quality control checks, broadly but superficially ○ The outcome requires further development in order to be suitable for the target market
6–11	○ Final outcome is largely complete and represents a basic level of making/modelling/finishing skills ○ Used materials, components and equipment correctly and safely (including CAM if appropriate) ○ Some aspects of outcome are demanding ○ Some evidence of limited quality control applied throughout the process ○ The outcome has some weaknesses which limit its suitability for the target market
0–5	○ Final outcome is incomplete or represents an undemanding level of making/modelling/finishing skills ○ Used materials, components and equipment safely under close supervision ○ Worked with some assistance to produce outcome of limited demand ○ There is limited evidence of any quality control and levels of accuracy are minimal ○ The outcome has significant weaknesses which limit its suitability for the target market

△ **Table 12.4** Making

At first sight it looks like all of the marks awarded in this section are given just for your manufactured piece. This is not the case. Within the body of your folder you should illustrate how you have used and selected the right materials and manufacturing techniques and how you have checked and tested quality issues.

To achieve high marks for this section you need to demonstrate the accurate use of a wide range of manufacturing skills. An analogy is that of a high diver in the Olympic Games: the first diver swallow dives head first into the pool perfectly vertically with a minimum splash. The second diver twists, turns and summersaults into the pool, not as vertically and with a larger splash. The second diver would gain the higher score, for the complexity of the dive. In the making section it is the same: you are being challenged to have a level of complexity in your work, as well as skill, technique and accuracy.

Knowledge link
Chapters 1, 2 and 11 will give you information on a variety of materials and manufacturing processes.

If you have a very simple design it will be difficult to build in a high level of making skills and use of a variety of materials and manufacturing

processes. At the design stage it is a good idea to reflect on this and ensure that your design meets the requirements of the brief and the demands of the making outcome.

The make must be manufactured and assembled accurately. It must have the correct level of demand. However, a balance should be set to ensure that it can be completed in the time allowed.

Testing and evaluating

Criterion 4 mark band	Testing and evaluation
9–12	○ Detailed testing and evaluation as appropriate throughout the designing and making process, taking account of client/user or third-party opinion ○ All aspects of the final outcome have been tested against the design criteria and/or the product/manufacturing specification ○ Evaluate and justify the need for modifications to the product and consideration given as to how the outcome might need to be modified for commercial production
6–8	○ Appropriate testing and evaluation evident throughout the designing and making process ○ Most aspects of the final outcome have been tested against the design criteria and/or the product/manufacturing specification ○ Evaluate and justify the need for improvements or modifications to the product
3–5	○ Evidence of some testing and evaluation leading to the production of the final outcome ○ Some evidence of testing against the design criteria and/or the product/manufacturing specification ○ Some improvements or modifications to product suggested
0–2	○ Minimal testing and evaluation throughout the designing and making process ○ Limited or no testing of final outcome against the design criteria and/or the product/manufacturing specification ○ Limited mention of some improvements or modifications that could be made to the product

△ **Table 12.5** Testing and evaluating

Plan of Making

Date.	The product or component.	Description of task.	Justify why the task needs to be in this position in your plan.	List the tools, processes and materials required.	Health and safety issues.	Quality control.	Est... time needed
Mon. 26/01	P.O.S Display	Create the locking mechanism for the back of the P.O.S.	To get an idea of if this mechanism can be done and if it is the best way style of mechanism.	Solid whiteboard, pencil, guillotine, steel rule, craft knife, glue and cutting mat.	Keep fingers away from the craft knife.	Use a guillotine to cut long straight edges.	1hour
Thurs. 29/01	P.O.S Display	Re-create the locking mechanism	To modify it and make it error free so it can be used for the final design.	Solid whiteboard, pencil, guillotine, steel rule, craft knife, glue and cutting mat.	Keep fingers away from the craft knife.	Use a guillotine to cut long straight edges.	1hour
Mon. 02/02	P.O.S Display	Creating the rabbit shape	To complete the prototype P.O.S display.	Solid whiteboard, pencil, scissors and fine liner.	Do not run with scissors. Keep fingers away from blades when cutting.	Keep to the lines and keep the outline neat.	15mins.
Mon 02/02	P.O.S Display	Scan rabbit shape	To get the P.O.S started on the computer.	Scanner and computer.	Keep liquids away from machinery.	N/A	10mins.
Mon 02/02	P.O.S Display	Vectorise Rabbit	To finalise the shape.	Computer and fireworks.	Keep liquids away from machinery.	CAD	5mins.
Mon 02/02	P.O.S Display	Create locking mechanism on 2D design tools.	It is the final part of the P.O.S display.	Computer and 2D Design Tools.	Keep liquids away from machinery.	CAD	30mins.
Thurs 05/02	P.O.S Display	Create a black rabbit shape out of card to put on top of the white, to give the colour specified.	To ensure the black rabbit shape is a correct fit.	Computer, 2D Design Tools, black card on a sacrificial base and a laser cutter.	Keep liquids away from the machinery. Do not try to pull out the material when in use.	CAD, laser cutter.	10mins
Thurs 05/02	P.O.S Display	Glue the black card rabbit shape and locking mechanism onto the P.O.S structure.	It is the final step in the P.O.S production.	Spray mount and P.O.S pre-made pieces.	Use spray mount in a well ventilated room.	Line up edges manually.	5-8mins
Thurs 05/02	CD Tray	Create the CD outline. Including the circles to hold the disc.	It is the starting point to create a CD tray. Everything which follows needs to fit around this requirement.	Computer, 2D Design Tools, disc and a ruler.	Keep liquids away from machinery.	CAD	30mins
Mon 16/02	CD Tray	Check the net for the CD.	To ensure that the measurements are correct.	Computer, 2D Design Tools, disc and a ruler.	Keep liquids away from machinery.	CAD	10mins

△ **Figure 12.23** Production plan

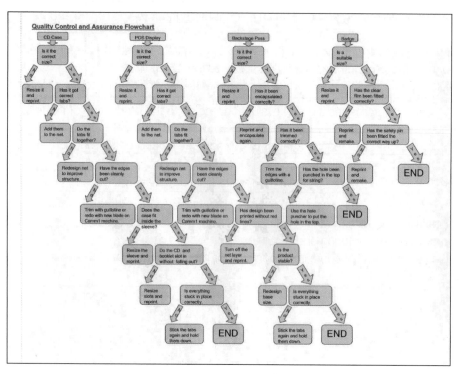

△ **Figure 12.24** Quality control and assurance flowchart

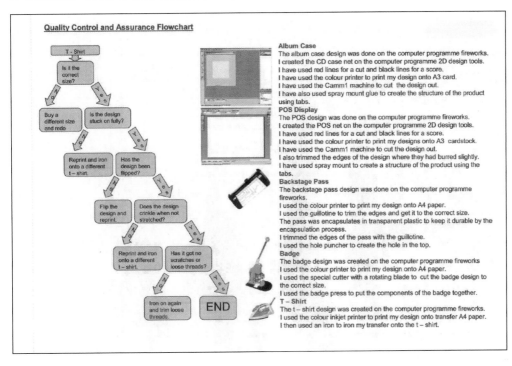

△ **Figure 12.25** Quality control and assurance flowchart

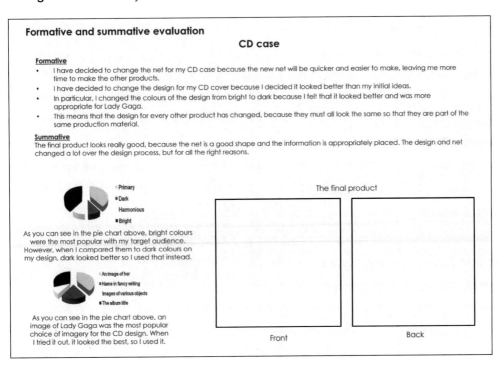

△ **Figure 12.26** Evaluation

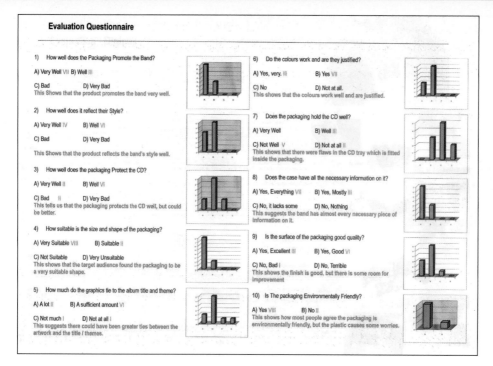

Evaluation Questionnaire

1) How well does the Packaging Promote the Band?

A) Very Well VII B) Well III

C) Bad   D) Very Bad
This Shows that the product promotes the band very well.

2) How well does it reflect their Style?

A) Very Well IV   B) Well VI

C) Bad   D) Very Bad
This Shows that the product reflects the band's style well.

3) How well does the packaging Protect the CD?

A) Very Well II   B) Well VI

C) Bad II   D) Very Bad
This tells us that the packaging protects the CD well, but could be better.

4) How suitable is the size and shape of the packaging?

A) Very Suitable VIII   B) Suitable II

C) Not Suitable   D) Very Unsuitable
This shows that the target audience found the packaging to be a very suitable shape.

5) How much do the graphics tie to the album title and theme?

A) A lot II   B) A sufficient amount VI

C) Not much I   D) Not at all I
This suggests there could have been greater ties between the artwork and the title / themes.

6) Do the colours work and are they justified?

A) Yes, very. III   B) Yes VII

C) No   D) Not at all.
This shows that the colours work well and are justified.

7) Does the packaging hold the CD well?

A) Very Well   B) Well III

C) Not Well V   D) Not at all II
This shows that there were flaws in the CD tray which is fitted inside the packaging.

8) Does the case have all the necessary information on it?

A) Yes, Everything VII   B) Yes, Mostly III

C) No, it lacks some   D) No, Nothing
This suggests the band has almost every necessary piece of information on it.

9) Is the surface of the packaging good quality?

A) Yes, Excellent III   B) Yes, Good VI

C) No, Bad I   D) No, Terrible
This shows the finish is good, but there is some room for improvement

10) Is The packaging Environmentally Friendly?

A) Yes VIII   B) No II
This shows how most people agree the packaging is environmentally friendly, but the plastic causes some worries.

△ **Figure 12.27** Evaluation questionnaire

Testing and evaluation are assessed throughout the whole of the design-and-make project. When developing your design, add evaluative comments; find ways of testing your product. For example, you could survey your target market on what they think of your block models, or test that a vacuumed inner for cosmetics packaging both holds the bottle and fits in the box. Test several types of card for printing or resistance to damage. You are expected to show the outline of the tests and most importantly the results and, as a consequence, your decisions.

Analyse your final product against the specification. Copy and paste it so that you ensure each point can be covered. Do not use a numeric scoring system alone; add comments to

justify your decisions. Remember at this stage it does not matter if it does not match exactly what you have stated; what is important is that you recognise and discuss the issues.

Think about how the product could be improved. A good starting point for this is if there is a shortfall against the specification points, or a comment given by your test user group. Good results in this section can be seen in further sketch sheets. Illustrate and annotate what you might do to improve your product.

Knowledge link
Chapter 6 will help you to test and evaluate your work.

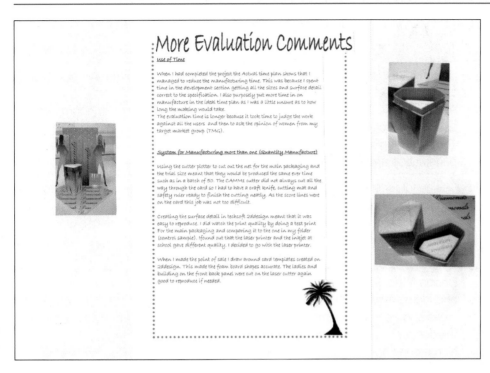

More Evaluation Comments

Use of Time

When I had completed the project the Actual time plan shows that I managed to reduce the manufacturing time. This was because I spent time in the development section getting all the sizes and surface detail correct to the specification. I also purposely put more time in on manufacture in the ideal time plan as I was a little unsure as to how long the making would take.

The evaluation time is longer because it took time to judge the work against all the users and then to ask the opinion of women from my target market group (TMG).

System for Manufacturing more than one (Quantity Manufacture)

Using the cutter plotter to cut out the net for the main packaging and the trial size meant that they would be produced the same ever time such as in a batch of 50. The CAMM1 cutter did not always cut all the way through the card so I had to have a craft knife, cutting mat and safety ruler ready to finish the cutting neatly. As the score lines were on the card this job was not too difficult.

Creating the surface detail in techsoft 2ddesign meant that it was easy to reproduce. I did watch the print quality by doing a test print. For the main packaging and comparing it to the one in my folder (control sample). I found out that the laser printer and the inkjet at school gave different quality. I decided to go with the laser printer.

When I made the point of sale I drew around card templates created on 2ddesign. This made the foam board shapes accurate. The ladies and building on the front back panel were cut on the laser cutter again good to reproduce if needed.

△ **Figure 12.28** Evaluation

Communication

The communication mark is given for the overall clarity, relevance, look, layout and general presentation of the folder. It should be obviously structured, follow the design process and convey to the reader the relevant information.

Ensure there is a wide range of accurate, detailed and illustrative skills. It is important to use a technical vocabulary throughout your folder. Make your writing legible, clear and in good English; also use correct spelling, punctuation, grammar and technical language. Many of these aspects can be aided by the use of a word processor.

Criterion 5 mark band	Communication
5–6	○ Design folder is focused, concise and relevant and demonstrates an appropriate selection of material for inclusion ○ All decisions communicated in a clear and coherent manner with appropriate use of technical language ○ The text is legible, easily understood and shows a good grasp of grammar, punctuation and spelling
3–4	○ Design folder shows some skill in choice of material for inclusion but includes some irrelevant content ○ Most decisions communicated with some clarity and with some use of technical language ○ There are a small number of errors in grammar, punctuation and spelling
0–2	○ Design folder shows excessive duplication of information and a lack of brevity and focus, resulting in irrelevant content ○ Ideas and decisions communicated at a simplistic level with a limited grasp of the concepts involved and a limited use of technical vocabulary ○ Numerous errors in grammar, punctuation and spelling

△ **Table 12.6** Communication

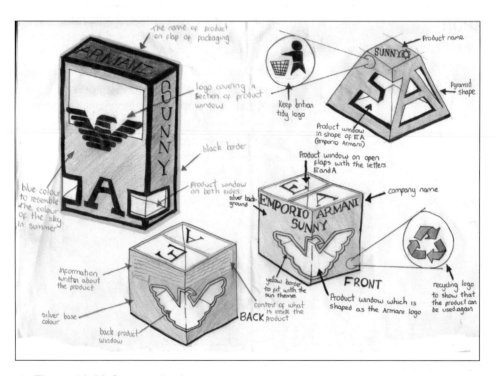

△ **Figure 12.29** Communication

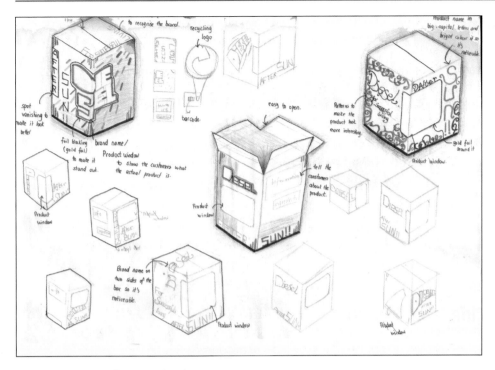

△ **Figure 12.30** Communication

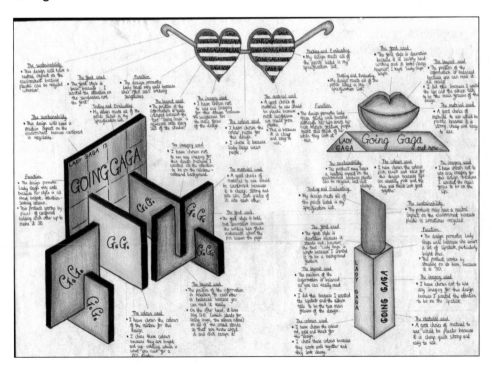

△ **Figure 12.31** Communication

12.4 **Creativity**

Being creative can be a difficult process. Often the mind will go blank, or everything seems as if it has been done before, or that it will not work. However, there are techniques that designers use to help the flow of innovate ideas.

Creativity can be a wasteful process. A lot of your early ideas will not work or will have flaws. At the initial stage do not worry about this; be prepared for wastage. Try not to stop illustrating an idea because you have thought of a problem with it. Put everything down on the page; you can be selective and logical after the concept has been generated. Often ideas are drawn and only one will have something that is worthwhile.

Connecting ideas and word association

If you were told that an idea you have generated was 'crazy' or 'whacky' you could feel a bit upset. Do not be concerned by this: linking different chains of thought can produce some inspirational ideas, as well as less successful ones. Often the links will be unworkable and look silly, but that is fine in this process. Remember: expect wastage.

A good example of the process of linking chains of thought is to consider the ramps on the end of the runway on aircraft carriers. The ramps allow heavier and bigger planes to take off from a short platform. This idea was generated from a ski jump. The designer saw that ski jumpers could fly a long distance because of the angle that they come off the ramp. He adapted this for use with aircraft. So, there is a link between the two seemingly unconnected ideas of ski jumping and ramps.

A technique to create these lateral ideas is to use word association. Think of three words related to your design. Write these down. Take each word in isolation and write the first three things that you associate with them. Then, take these three words and do the same, and so on. Soon you

will have a huge collection of words. Randomly take two pairs and illustrate them; do this several times. You will develop a selection of innovative illustrations based around your product's theme.

As an example, consider a new logo for a cosmetics company called 'Desert Mist'. Figure 12.32 shows a chart the designer of the cosmetics company has created using word association.

Activity

Using the chart in Figure 12.32, two random words have been chosen and combined as follows:

o Gold dragon
o Tartan sandcastles
o Ice candles
o Fluffy knife
o Snow dunes

Illustrate each of these ideas.

The golden dragon is a possible concept. Imagine a drawing of a golden dragon wrapped around the box for the Desert Mist perfume. This concept would not have been considered if we had not completed the word association exercise above.

Mixing parts of a design

By mixing up key parts of a design, some of the permutations might not work for your product (known as **creative wastage**), but lots of new ideas can be generated quickly by this method.

A good example of this is the rear light cluster on cars. The functions are brake light, indicator and reverse light. There are thousands of examples of how, by changing the size, shape and position of each of these three elements, a different design is achieved.

We can use this technique in our design thinking. Begin by identifying three features of your product. For example, on the perfume packaging shown in Figure 12.33, the three features are the cosmetics company name, the perfume name and the artwork.

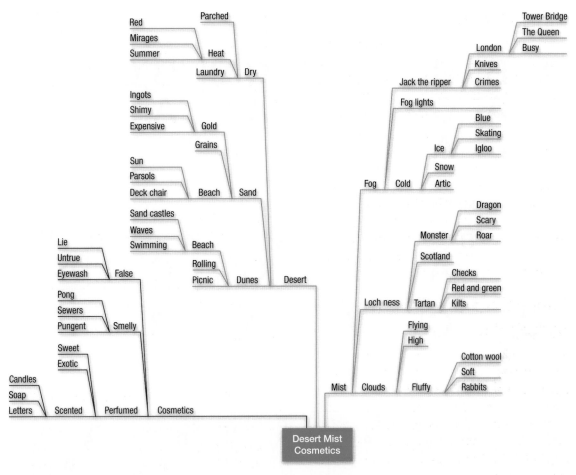

△ **Figure 12.32** Word association for Desert Mist Cosmetics

△ **Figure 12.33** Perfume packaging

A simplified layout of this is shown in Figure 12.34.

These can be mixed up to give the layout permutations shown in Figure 12.35.

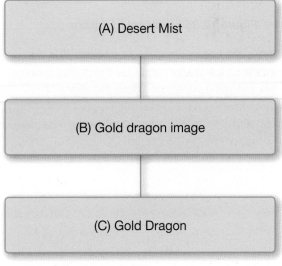

△ **Figure 12.34** simplified layout

Linear

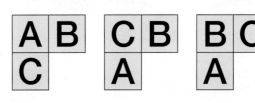

Perfendicular

Partly Embedded

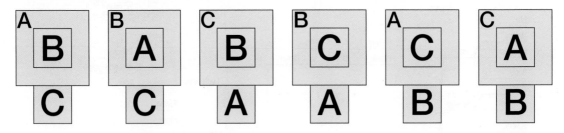

Fully Embedded

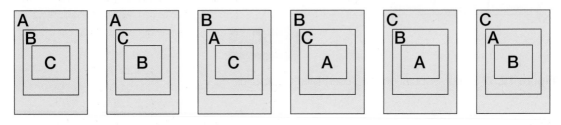

△ **Figure 12.35** Layout permutations

If A is the cosmetics company name, B is the
image of the dragon and C is the perfume name,
we can get a variety of different designs.

△ **Figure 12.36** Different variations of the same design

Activity

1. Choose three of the permutations above. Sketch these layouts on a blank piece of paper. (These sketches can be thumbnail in size.) As a simple line drawing, draw the layout of the components to give an impression of how the product would look. Within a short space of time you should have several original ideas.

2. To further develop these designs, try changing the proportion or the shape of the components.

Evaluation

An evaluation wheel is a graphical way of expressing your comments on your product. Two concentric circles are drawn and are then split equally into three, radiating out from the centre point.

The three sections are labelled as the manufacturer, the user and the client. Consider what each of these three groups would feel about your product. In the inner circle write positive comments, in the outer circle note the negative comments. This method of showing evaluation gives a strong graphic image of your evaluative comments.

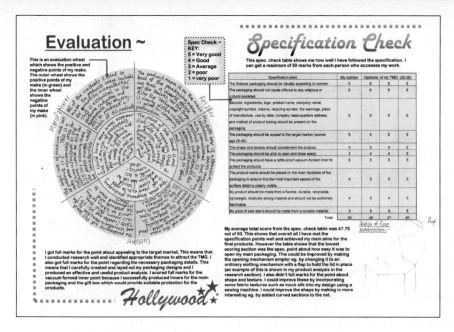

△ **Figure 12.37** Evaluative wheel

Index